A TREASURY OF

The World's Great Myths and Legends

A Treasury

of the World's Great

Myths and Legends

FOR BOYS AND GIRLS

by Joanna Strong and Tom B. Leonard

with illustrations by Hubert Whatley

HART PUBLISHING COMPANY, NEW YORK CITY

Contents

List of Illustrations

9

PAGE

A TREASURY OF
The World's Great Myths and Legends

The Trojan Horse

THE TRICK THAT WON A WAR

THE famous Trojan war had been raging for nine long years. The great struggle had started when Paris, son of the king of Troy, had fallen in love with the beautiful Helen, wife of Menelaus, King of Sparta. Paris kidnapped Helen, and carried her off to Troy. King Menelaus called upon his allies, the kings of all his neighboring countries, to help him rescue his Queen. Together, the kings of Greece fitted out an army and set forth to battle against Troy and rescue Helen.

After much fighting, the Greeks had finally surrounded the city of Troy. Food became scarce in the city. People were starving, but still the Trojans bravely fought on—fought on for many long months.

It began to look as though the Greeks would never conquer Troy. Then Ulysses, the Greek general, thought of a clever plan. Far from the city, Ulysses had his men build an enormous wooden horse. Then he had the Greeks fill the horse with hundreds of armed soldiers. One night, the Greeks pulled the horse across the fields and placed it just outside the city walls. Then they got into their ships, and sailed a short distance away so that it should seem as if they had given up the siege.

The next morning, the watchers on the walls of Troy let out a cry, "Praise be to Jupiter! The Greeks have gone! The siege is over! We are saved!"

They threw open the huge gates and the people rushed out. Oh! how happy they were. Now they would be able to get food! Now they would be able to get plenty of fresh water!

Suddenly they saw the enormous horse. What could it be? Some of the leaders of the city said, "Burn it—it is some sort of a trick." Just then a group of Trojan soldiers came along, dragging a prisoner. They had found a Greek soldier hiding in the woods nearby. The Greek trembled with terror and begged the Trojans not to kill him. He said he had run away from his army because he was certain that the Greeks were going to lose the war. He told the Trojans that the tremendous wooden horse was made by the Greeks as an offering to the gods.

"Why," the Trojan commanders demanded to know, "why was the horse built so large?" The captured soldier replied that the animal had been made so huge on purpose, so that the Trojans could not take it into their city.

When the people of Troy heard this, they made up their minds that they would take the horse into the city in spite of the Greeks. Tremendous ropes were made and tied to the horse. Hundreds of

Silently, they let down ladders.

Trojan citizens gathered round and pulled and tugged and pushed and sweated until at last the horse stood inside the city walls.

Then the Trojans held a great feast. They rejoiced that they were finally rescued from the Greeks and that the war was now over. All day long the Trojans, soldiers and civilians alike, ate and drank. When night came, most of them were so full of food and wine that they lay down wherever they were and fell fast asleep. Even the guards were drowsing at their posts.

Then when all was quiet in the sleeping city, the Greek soldiers inside the wooden horse swung open the concealed doors. Silently, they let down ladders. Then they climbed down, rushed to the city gates, and threw them wide open.

Thousands of Greek soldiers from the ships lay in waiting. The invaders poured in through the opened gates to join their comrades in arms. Then, the attack began!

The Trojans, taken completely by surprise, were overcome. Troy was laid waste. King Menelaus rescued his kidnapped Queen, and took Helen back to Sparta.

So it was, that whereas all the strength of the Greeks could not overcome Troy, the foolish curiosity of the Trojans themselves proved their undoing.

Jason and The Golden Fleece

THE VOYAGE OF THE ARGONAUTS

OLD King Aeson of Thessaly was worn and weary with the heavy cares of governing his people. He longed to have his handsome little son, Jason, take his place on the throne. But Jason was young, much too young to rule over a kingdom. Yet the king was too old and too tired to go on.

So Aeson called his brother, Pelias, before him and said: "My brother, I can no longer rule. While my little son, Jason, is still a child, I would have you take the throne in my place. But you must agree that when Jason reaches manhood, he, the rightful ruler, shall be king."

Pelias readily agreed. But secretly he made up his mind that Jason would never be seated upon the throne of Thessaly. To find out just how he might keep the kingdom for himself, Pelias went to an oracle. The oracles were fortune-tellers. In those days, people believed that an oracle had the mystic power to see into the future.

After mumbling a few charms and burning some magic powders, the oracle told Pelias, "Fear not anyone who cometh not with and without a shoe!"

This strange reply satisfied Pelias that he had nothing to fear from Jason. But to make doubly sure that Jason would never cause him trouble, after the old King Aeson died, Pelias had Jason banished to a far-away land, many weeks' journey from Thessaly.

There in that far off country, Jason was reared. He grew from babyhood into boyhood; and when it came time for Jason to go to school, he was sent to study with the centaurs. A centaur was a strange creature, half man and half horse. Below the waist, the centaur had the four legs and body of a horse, which gave him the speed and strength of that animal. From the waist up, the centaur was a man, gifted with the intelligence of men. The centaurs were famous for being very learned. In addition they were known for their tremendous bravery and skill as fighters and archers.

Young Jason's special teacher was Chiron, the chief of the centaurs. Chiron was delighted with Jason's wit and quickness. Chiron taught so well, and Jason learned so readily, that soon the youth was a master of the manly arts, and had a goodly store of the world's wisdom.

Jason did not know that he was a king's son. But when the young prince reached manhood, Chiron the centaur, satisfied that Jason was fit to be a king, told him the story of his royal birth. Jason determined to win his throne back from his wicked uncle, Pelias.

So Chiron consulted an oracle for advice on how Jason should overcome his uncle. Again came a strange reply:

"Who seeks the crown shall wear a leopard's hide!" said the oracle.

Heeding the oracle's words, Jason ventured deep into the forest and killed a leopard. Then Jason dressed himself in the leopard's skin. He said farewell to Chiron, and set forth on his way to Thessaly.

Soon Jason came to a rushing river. The stream was so wide and deep, and its current so strong, that the people who stood on the river bank warned Jason not to try to cross. Many men had tried, the people said, but no man had been able to cross the river alive.

Undaunted, Jason stepped into the raging current. The swirling waters pulled angrily at the young man who dared defy its power. The trunks of huge trees, being carried down the stream, rushed at Jason like mad things. One slip—one moment of carelessness—and Jason would go down, never to be seen again. Step by step he made his way across, while those who watched from the river's banks held their breath. There were only three steps, two steps, one step more to go—when suddenly the watchers saw Jason swept off his feet!

A groan went up from many lips. The brave young man who had braved the torrent was lost! But no! One powerful arm reached up and grasped a large branch of a tree which overhung the river. Slowly Jason pulled himself to safety on the far bank of the river. He had won his first great test!

Jason rested but a moment. Then he stood up. Suddenly he

realized that one of his feet was bare. He had lost one of his sandals in the rushing river. But eager to reach Thessaly, he strode forward.

It was not long before Jason came to his own city. As he walked through the streets of Thessaly, clad only in a leopard skin and one sandal, a great commotion arose. People, seeing this handsome youth, remembered the old prophecy that a young man would appear, wearing only one sandal, and that he would be their rightful king.

The false king pretended that he was glad to see Jason. Pelias said he had only been holding Jason's kingdom for him until his return and that he would be glad now to turn the throne over to the returning Prince.

Then Pelias beguiled Jason with a royal feast of welcome. With his nephew in fine humor, Pelias craftily told Jason of a glorious adventure which would make the youth famous all over the world. "Far away, in the land of Colchis, there is a Golden Fleece," he said. "This fleece is the skin of a golden sheep which is the rightful property of your family. But the Golden Fleece is held by the king of Colchis. It is guarded by a dragon which never sleeps. If I were a young man, nothing would stop me from winning the Golden Fleece."

When Jason heard this story, he was determined to win fame and glory by capturing the Golden Fleece. This was just as Pelias planned, for he was sure that Jason would be killed on this dangerous quest.

Jason issued a call for brave men to accompany him on his adventure. From all parts of Greece they came. Jason chose only the bravest and the best. Soon there were assembled in Thessaly fifty of the greatest heroes of Greece.

Jason commissioned Argus, a famous boatbuilder, to build him a ship, large enough to hold fifty men. Argus built a vessel, the like of which had never been seen before. It was strong and large.

When their ship was finished, the heroes called it the *Argo*, after Argus, the builder; and they themselves were called the Argonauts. Thus equipped, the fifty heroes set forth from Thessaly with Jason at their head. Good fortune seemed to favor them, for when the Argonauts came to Thrace, they were forewarned by Phineus, the sage, of a great danger which lay before them.

In the sea over which they had to sail were two rocky islands between which they must pass. But whenever anything passed between these islands, they would come crashing together with such speed that anything caught between the two islands was crushed to splinters.

"To avoid this terrible catastrophe," said Phineus, "when you approach the islands, let loose a dove. The dove, flying between the islands will cause them to rush together, but she can fly through swiftly enough to escape destruction. Then, at the moment when the islands start returning to their former places, you and your men lay to the oars, and row with all your might. With the help of the gods you may be fast enough to get through before the islands rush together again."

Jason and his companions thanked Phineus and continued on their way. Soon they came to the islands. The Argonauts drew as near to the fearful passage as possible. Then they released the dove. Straight as an arrow the bird flew between the islands. A roaring sound filled their ears as the islands came rushing together with a crash. But the dove was safe; only her tail feathers were caught between the rocky walls of the islands.

Jason's men sat alertly at the oars, ready at Jason's signal to row with all their strength. The moment the islands had separated enough for the *Argo* to fit through, Jason gave the signal. Then, as one man, the Argonauts plied their oars. The sweat stood out on every brow as they pulled. Swift as a bird the *Argo*, with its crew of heroes, sped between the islands. The islands separated their full distance, and then with fearful speed, came crashing together again. By just the breadth of a hair, the *Argo* slipped through. Actually, the tip of the dreadful islands grazed the stern of the boat.

The brave young men offered thanks to the gods, and thought of Phineus with gratitude for their deliverance. Then they sailed on.

At last the heroes came to the kingdom of Colchis. Jason made known to the king his determination to get the Golden Fleece. The king laughed.

"O ho, you think that all you have to do is come here and demand the Golden Fleece and it is yours! Not so fast, my young fellow. Do you not know that the first thing you must do is to harness the fire breathing bulls? Then you must plow the stony field which

Quick as a flash, Jason threw the stone . . .

lies next to the temple of Mars. After that you must sow the dragon's teeth in the field. Then we shall see what happens." And the king laughed a scornful laugh, which warned Jason that great trials and dangers lay ahead for the Argonauts.

But Jason was not frightened or discouraged. "Let us not delay a moment," he cried. "Lead us to our tasks!"

So the king led Jason and his companions to the field of the bulls. The fierce red eyes of the bulls glared angrily at Jason and his bold crew. As the bulls pawed the ground, the fiery breath which curled from their nostrils, scorched the ground for many yards around them. No man could get close enough to harness the ferocious beasts without being burned to a crisp by the flames they breathed out. The Argonauts were forced to withdraw from the field.

That night, in the Argonauts' encampment, Jason was in despair. Suddenly there stood before him a maiden. It was the king's daughter, Medea. She had fallen in love with Jason.

"Do not be downhearted," she said. "No mortal man, unaided, could have overcome these enchanted bulls. But I can help you. If you promise to marry me and carry me off with you, I will help you to win the Golden Fleece." Jason agreed.

Then she gave him a magic herb. "This will tame the bulls," she said.

Next, she gave him a heavy black stone, saying, "Use this when the need arises."

At dawn, the next morning, Jason went into the field alone.

When the bulls came stamping towards him, he held out the magic herb and lo! the bulls became tame! They crouched gently at Jason's feet and permitted him to yoke them to the plow.

When the king and his court arose, there was Jason, quietly plowing the field of Mars with the now gentle bulls.

The king was furious, and suspected treachery, but he never suspected his own daughter.

"Here," he said, "in this warrior's helmet are the dragon's teeth. Sow them in the field you have plowed."

Jason took the helmet and did as he was bid. No sooner had he strewn the seeds in the furrows than little shiny points began to appear. As Jason watched, the points grew. Soon, to his horror, he saw a most remarkable thing. Each of the teeth which he had sown was becoming an armed warrior. First their spears appeared; then their helmets and, right under his eyes, Jason saw an army of soldiers come up out of the ground. No sooner had they sprouted, than the soldiers brandished their spears and rushed upon him. Jason drew his sword to fight, but how could one man hope to win against so many?

Then he remembered the weapon Medea had given him. The stone. That was it! Now must be the time to use it!

Quick as a flash, Jason threw the stone right into the midst of the army. The man who was hit, sure that his neighbor had struck him, turned angrily and struck him back. In a matter of moments, the thousand soldiers who had sprung from the dragon's teeth were fighting each other. They fought each other, instead of Jason, until not one of the army was left alive.

Now the king's daughter quickly drew near to Jason.

"Quick!" whispered Medea. "To the fleece!"

She handed Jason a magic potion.

Jason rushed to the garden where the fleece, guarded by the dragon who never slept, was hanging on a tree.

Jason sprinkled a few drops of the potion before the dragon, and its hideous head rolled from side to side as it fell into a deep sleep. Then Jason drew his sword and cut off the dragon's head. He looked about him and there hanging on the limb of a tree, was the Golden Fleece. It gleamed like the sun. Jason seized the precious prize and shouted to his comrades to follow him to their ship. Medea, too, made for the ship, for she well knew what her fate would be when her father discovered her part in helping Jason—as he surely would.

In a rage, the king gathered together his men and pursued his daughter and the Argonauts, hoping to catch them before they reached their ship. But the Argonauts were too swift and too strong for the king's men, and they made good their escape.

The *Argo*, with its dauntless crew, had many perilous moments on the return voyage, but with the help of the gods, who applauded their bravery, they at last reached Thessaly again.

Now, with the help of the fifty heroes, Jason forced the evil King Pelias to yield the kingdom to him, its rightful ruler.

Daedalus and Icarus

THE MEN WHO FLEW LIKE BIRDS

O N the island of Crete, during the reign of King Minos, there lived a most skillful artisan named Daedalus. Daedalus was the greatest inventor and craftsman of his time, and his fame spread to the far corners of the world.

It was Daedalus who built the famous labyrinth in which King Minos kept that terrible beast, the Minotaur. This labyrinth was a building with hundreds of winding halls and passages, so complicated that no one who went into it could ever find his way out again.

But although Daedalus performed great services for King Minos, the king feared him. Minos was afraid that Daedalus with his great wisdom and skill, might some day gain the throne of Crete. So King Minos caused Daedalus and his young son, Icarus, to be imprisoned in a dark, stone tower.

But no locks could hold Daedalus! For he could open them all. And one dark night Daedalus and young Icarus escaped from the tower.

Down he fell into the sea!

After they had fled, Daedalus and Icarus did not find it so easy to escape from Crete. You see, Crete is an island, and King Minos had his soldiers search every ship that left its shores.

Daedalus and Icarus lay in hiding in a cave along the seashore. One bright day, Daedalus was idly watching the sea gulls soaring and swooping over the water in their search for food. Suddenly an idea struck him.

"King Minos may control the land and the sea," he cried, "but he does not control the air. That is how Icarus and I shall escape."

Then Daedalus set to work to study the birds and learn the secret of their flight. For endless hours he watched the birds flying. He caught a bird and studied the clever structure of its wings. Then he put to use his knowledge and skill to copy the wings of a bird. The boy, Icarus, spent his days trapping the sea gulls and plucking their feathers. Daedalus took the feathers which his son had obtained, and sewed them together with marvelous skill. Soon wings began to take shape, so wonderfully made that, except for their great size, they looked exactly like the real wings of a bird. And then Daedalus took these wings, and with melted wax attached them to a wooden framework.

When he had made a pair of wings for himself and a pair of wings for his son, Daedalus fastened them in place. A wing was strapped to each arm. Then Daedalus proceeded to teach his son to fly, just as a mother bird teaches her young. How happy and excited young Icarus was when he found that he could fly through the air, that he could circle and float on the wind! He was impatient to be off.

Finally the time came when Daedalus felt they were ready to make the escape from Crete. He turned to his young son and said, "Icarus, listen carefully to my words. Follow close behind me in your flight. Do not fly too low or the dampness from the sea will cling to your wings and make them too heavy for you to lift. Do not fly too high or the sun will melt the wax of your wings."

Then Daedalus kissed his son fondly and began to rise into the air. Icarus followed his father. As the two of them flew across the sky, people looked up in amazement. The ploughmen in the fields gazed upward, the shepherds marveled! They thought they were watching the flight of gods.

At first, Icarus stayed close behind his father. But then, exulting in his new-found power, he flew off on little side trips. Soon he forgot everything his father had told him and flew high into the heavens.

Then the blazing sun did its work and the wax of his wings melted. Icarus fluttered his arms, but there were not enough feathers left to beat the air. He called his father, but in vain. Down he fell into the sea!

Daedalus sped to the aid of his son, but when he saw the feathers floating on the ocean, he knew to his grief that Icarus had been drowned. So ended man's first attempt to fly; for Daedalus, heartbroken at the loss of his son, flew on to Sicily, took off his wings and never flew again.

The Story of Theseus

THE BRAVE YOUTH WHO FREED A KINGDOM

IN the kingdom of Athens there once lived a good king named Aegeus. He journeyed many miles from Athens to marry a beautiful princess named Aethra, who lived in a far-away land.

Alas! Before the time came for King Aegeus to return to Athens with his lovely queen, a messenger arrived bearing terrible news. The kingdom of Athens had been attacked by the armies of King Minos of Crete!

With sorrow in his heart, King Aegeus knew he must leave his bride behind in her father's kingdom. Before he bade her farewell, however, he led her to the top of a hill, on which there lay a mighty stone.

"I can stay no longer, dear wife," he said. "The child you will bear in a short time, I cannot see. I know not how long this war will last, or how long it will be before I can come for you. But see, under this stone I have placed a sword and a pair of sandals. When our son is strong enough to lift this stone and take the sword and sandals for himself, let him come to me in Athens."

Then Aegeus kissed his wife and set forth for the besieged land.

Soon a son was born to Queen Aethra. She named him Theseus. The young prince was brought up as befitted a king's son in those warlike days. He was taught to ride the most spirited horses, taught to shoot an arrow straight and true, and taught to handle a sword with skill and daring. Soon there were none more proficient in the arts of war than Theseus.

The years passed swiftly, but Aegeus did not return for his queen, and she could not know what misfortune had befallen him, or his kingdom of Athens. But with the years, the young prince Theseus grew in beauty and courage and strength.

Queen Aethra heeded her husband's instructions. There came a day when she felt it was time to test the strength of their son, Prince Theseus. On that day, mother and son walked up the hill to the place where King Aegeus had hidden the sword and sandals.

"My son," said she, "Can you lift this stone?"

Without a word, the young man leaned down. With astonishing ease Theseus lifted the enormous stone, and looked wonderingly at the jewel-encrusted sword and handsome gold sandals that lay underneath.

"Ah, my son, the time has come for us to part! Now you are a man. You have just proven that. And as a man, you must go to your father, my husband, Aegeus, the King of Athens. The way is long and dangerous, but you have strength, and youth, and courage. May good fortune follow you."

So saying, his mother bade him farewell. Then Theseus kissed her fondly and set out for his father's kingdom.

The first day's journey brought Theseus into the land where dwelled Epidaurus, the robber giant. Epidaurus, the Club-carrier, he was called, for in his hand he always swung a towering iron club. Many an innocent wayfarer had been waylaid and beaten to death by this wicked giant.

From afar, Epidaurus spied the handsome young Theseus as he swung cheerfully along the highroad.

"O ho!" chortled the robber, "here's a rich prize! An elegant young nobleman he must be, for look at his fine clothes. It will be a moment's work to club this namby-pamby lad and pocket his gold. I'll hide behind this clump of trees, and boff! That will be the end of him!"

But Theseus was no fool. Warily he approached the clump of trees, keeping his ears alert for any suspicious sound. Epidaurus sprang! But Theseus was ready for him. Nimbly dodging the blow of the fearful iron club, Theseus stretched out his foot and sent the clumsy giant sprawling. The club flashed past Theseus' head, and with a mighty thud buried itself harmlessly in the ground. Quick as a wink Theseus leaped on Epidaurus. Before the robber could regain his balance, Theseus wrenched the club from his powerful hands. Again the giant lunged, and again Theseus sidestepped. Now the young prince, his muscles straining, lifted the giant's club. The tip flashed in the sunlight as Theseus lifted it over his head. Then, crash! Try as he might, the robber giant could not escape that mighty blow. It landed fair on the robber's brow, and with a groan he sank to earth, and breathed his last. No longer would Epidaurus terrorize innocent travelers!

Athens was not many days journey away, when Theseus met up with the terrible man called Procrustes the Stretcher. Procrustes had a house in a lonely spot along the road. When a footsore traveler passed that way, Procrustes would welcome him cunningly, with false smiles and deceiving words. He would offer the weary wayfarer food and drink and rest. But no one ever left Procrustes' dreadful house alive. In the house Procrustes had an iron bed which, he boasted, would just fit anyone who lay on it. Sure enough it did. For no sooner had the traveler fallen asleep on the bed, when iron arms came down and clamped him in place. Then if the stranger were longer than the bed, Procrustes would chop off his limbs; if he were shorter than the bed, the pitiless monster would stretch the traveler's limbs to fit the length.

But Procrustes met his match in Theseus. When Procrustes led Theseus to the terrible iron bed, the young prince pretended he did not know how to lie in it. The wicked Procrustes lay down on the bed himself to show Theseus what to do. Whereupon Theseus leaped on Procrustes, and taking him by surprise, tied his arms and legs to the bed. Then Theseus treated Procrustes exactly as Procrustes had treated so many others.

When at last the city of Athens loomed ahead, Theseus sped

on with joy in his heart. He could not know that his most dangerous adventure still lay ahead of him.

In Athens, where Theseus expected to find only joy at his arrival, he found instead sadness. Of course King Aegeus was happy to see his stalwart son, but in his heart there was a great sorrow for his kingdom and his people.

"You have come at a sad and troublous time," the King told Theseus." I must tell you that Athens was conquered in war by King Minos of Crete. And now we must pay him a terrible price. Every year we must send seven of our noblest youths and seven of our loveliest maidens to the Island of Crete to be devoured by the Minotaur."

When Theseus heard this he cried, "My father, choose me to be one of the seven youths. I will go to Crete and slay the Minotaur."

"Oh, no, my son! You are the hope of Athens. You must be king when I die. Do not ask me to send you to your death!"

But Theseus answered, "Athens will die if its courage dies. I will go."

So in spite of his father's pleas, Theseus made ready to sail. The dread day of departure came, and the ship with its gloomy black sail was ready to lift anchor.

As Theseus said farewell to his father, he said, "This ship will surely return with everyone safe, believe it. And when we do, we shall change the black sail for a white sail. In that way you will know the good news from afar off, and you will rejoice."

"I shall be praying and watching," said King Aegeus.

In Crete, as the Athenian youths and maidens were marched through the streets to their prison, many people lined the way to look at them. There were many who were sorry for them when they saw how young they were. Not so King Minos. He gloated over his triumph, and said to his lovely daughter Ariadne, who was standing with him, "See, this is the way I make sure that the Kingdom of Athens will never be strong again. The Minotaur will destroy their strongest and best while they are still young. They will never have a leader." But the young princess felt pity for them in her heart. "They are too young and noble to die," she mourned.

Then her eyes rested on the young hero, Theseus, and straightway she fell in love with him. She could not bear the thought that this tall young man, who stood like a king, should be devoured by the vile Minotaur. She must find a way to help him.

That night the door of Theseus' prison cell creaked open. A beautiful girl stepped into the room.

Theseus rose in wonder. "Fair maiden, who are you?" he asked, "and why have you come to my cell?"

"I am Ariadne, the daughter of the king," she answered, "and I have come to help you."

Then she handed him a sword and a ball of silken thread.

"The sword is for you to kill the ferocious Minotaur. The thread is your means of escape. Of what use would it be for you to kill the Minotaur and then die of hunger as you tried in vain to find your

. . . with a terrifying bellow, he charged.

way out of the labyrinth? But if you tie one end of the strong thread to the doorpost of the labyrinth and unwind it as you make your way through the passages to find the beast, you will have a silken clue which will lead you out again in safety."

"Why have you done this? Why do you help me?" said Theseus.

"Can you not tell?" said Ariadne.

"Beautiful princess, if I did not love you for your beauty, I would love you for your goodness. I will slay the Minotaur. See that my ship is ready. Wait for me at the door of the labyrinth. I will take you with me to Athens and make you my wife."

Ariadne hastened away, with her heart full of hope. The next day, Theseus and his companions were led into the labyrinth. Theseus hid the sword and the ball of thread under his cloak. He did as Ariadne had told him, and tied one end of the thread to the doorpost. Then he stepped boldly into the labyrinth and waited.

At last, they heard a distant sound of bellowing. Their hearts froze within them.

"He is coming!" shouted Theseus. He drew his sword.

Around the end of the passage came the Minotaur. He was twice as tall as a man with the head of a monstrous bull. He roared and rushed at the frightened Athenians. But when the Minotaur saw Theseus, instead of running away, advancing to meet him, he reared back for a moment. No one had ever defied the terrible beast before. Then the Minotaur lowered his head, and with a terrifying bellow, he charged. Theseus leaped aside, thrusting at the monster with his sword as he leaped. The savage blow cut off the leg of the Minotaur; and as the beast, bellowing and rolling about in his pain tried to charge into Theseus with his sharp horns, Theseus pierced him through his heart. With an earth shaking shudder, the Minotaur fell back dead.

Then the youths and maidens fell on their knees before Theseus. They kissed his hands in gratitude and swore eternal love to him for their rescue.

It was now almost night. Theseus, bidding the others follow him, wound the ball of thread as it led him through the endless corridors. At last they were at the gate and there stood Ariadne, with her arms outstretched in joy.

Under cover of the night, they made their way to the ship, and as quickly as possible, set sail for home.

Back in Athens, King Aegeus was watching for their ship. Would it come back with black sails, telling of the death of his son and the others? Or would the ship have white sails, bearing a joyous message that all was well?

At last the vessel came into the harbor. But in the rejoicing that took place aboard the ship, they had forgotten to change the sail!

"Alas," cried Aegeus, "my son is dead! What joy is there left for me in this world?" And with that Aegeus flung himself into the sea and was drowned. And that sea, from then on, even until the present day is called the Aegean Sea.

So Theseus became King of Athens, and ruled wisely and well.

Ulysses and the Cyclops

DEATH BATTLE WITH A MONSTER

ONE of the longest and most terrible wars of ancient time was the nine years' war between the Greeks and the Trojans. In that war, perhaps the greatest of the Greek generals was King Ulysses of Ithaca. It was his clever strategy which finally resulted in the capture of Troy and victory for the besieging Greek armies.

Anxious to return to Ithaca and to his dear wife and child from whom he had so long been separated, Ulysses lost no time in setting sail for home. But the storms battered the king's frail vessel, and unfavorable winds drove it far from its course. It was with great relief that they finally sighted an unfamiliar island where Ulysses thought they might obtain fresh supplies.

With a small group of men, Ulysses went ashore and set out to explore the island. With them, they carried a cask of wine as a friendship gift for whomever they might meet. They had not gone far when they chanced upon a large cave. Imagine their delight upon entering it to find that it was piled high with all kinds of food!

But the Greeks would scarcely have been so overjoyed had they known that the island was inhabited by a fierce race of giants called the Cyclops. Each of these strange and hideous creatures had a single enormous eye set in the center of his forehead.

Ulysses and his men however did not know what manner of creatures these Cyclops were, so their joy at finding the well-stocked cave was unrestrained. Suddenly a vast shadow fell across the entrance to the cave, blocking out all sunlight! Polyphemus, the inhabitant of the cave had returned, driving his flocks before him.

A single glance at the one-eyed monster was enough to make the Greeks gasp in horror. Quaking with terror, they clustered together at the back of the cave while Polyphemus drove his flock through the entrance. Then, entering the cave himself, the Cyclops closed off the entrance with a stone so huge that twenty oxen could not have budged it.

As his one great eye accustomed itself to the dim light, Polyphemus suddenly became aware of his unexpected visitors.

"Who are you?" he demanded to know in a voice that echoed like thunder, "And why come you here?"

Ulysses stepped forward. "We are Greeks," he answered humbly. "We are returning home from a war in which we have won much glory. In the name of the gods, we pray your hospitality."

Polyphemus gave no answer save to reach out his enormous hands and seize two of Ulysses' men. As the unfortunate pair struggled in terror, the giant hurled them against the wall of the cave, killing them instantly.

In helpless horror the Greeks watched the giant devour their two unlucky companions. Then the monster stretched himself on the floor of the cave and went to sleep.

Ulysses jumped up and drew his sword. This was his chance to kill the Cyclops as he slept. But then he realized that all his men together did not have the strength to push away the stone that blocked the mouth of the cave. If they killed Polyphemus, they would all be buried alive!

When morning came, the giant again seized two of Ulysses' companions, killed them in the same way, and ate them. He then moved the enormous stone from the cave entrance, drove out his flocks, and carefully replaced the stone. Polyphemus was taking no chance that Ulysses and his men would escape while he was gone.

But Ulysses' nimble mind had already set to work on a plan for escape. He had his men take the huge bar of wood, big as the trunk of a tree, which the giant had used as a staff, and whittle the end of it to a point with their swords. Ulysses placed the pointed end in the fire until it was red hot. Then the Greeks hid it in a dark corner of the cave.

When Polyphemus returned, they had to stand by powerless once again while the giant murdered and devoured two more of their number. Then Ulysses approached the brute and offered him a bowl of wine drawn from the cask which they had carried from the ship. "Cyclops, this is good wine," said Ulysses. "Take it as a gift from me."

The giant took the bowl, drained it at a gulp, and smacked his lips. "I find this good," said Polyphemus to Ulysses. "Let me have more. As your reward, I promise you shall be the last one I devour. What is your name?"

"Noman is my name," said Ulysses, as he handed the giant another bowl of wine. Again and again, Ulysses filled the bowl until the giant fell over in a drunken stupor, and lay snoring.

Then Ulysses with four of his companions lifted up the wooden bar with its red-hot point and buried it deep into the Cyclops' eye. Round and round they twirled it, while the giant shrieked in pain.

The howling monster filled the cave with such an outcry that the other Cyclops heard him bellow. They rushed to his aid, demanding to know what was the matter.

"O friends," cried the giant, "I die and Noman has given the blow!"

The other Cyclops answered, "Well, then, if no man has given the blow, it is a stroke from the gods and there is nothing we can do. You must bear it." And they left.

The infuriated giant tried to catch Ulysses and his men, but since Polyphemus was now blind the Greeks found it easy to elude his groping hands.

Next morning, the Cyclops again rolled away the stone to let his flocks out to pasture. But now the only way he could prevent his prisoners from escaping was by his sense of touch. He planted himself at the entrance of the cave to feel each of his sheep as they went

. . . Polyphemus tore a huge stone from the mountainside . . .

out, to make sure no man was among them.

But Ulysses had foreseen this, too. Clinging desperately with hands and knees, each of the Greeks swung himself under one of the rams. As each animal walked out of the cave, the blind and vengeful giant felt their backs and sides. But the Cyclops did not think to reach under them.

So Ulysses and his few remaining companions escaped. Then they drove Polyphemus' flocks down to their ship. Loading the animals aboard with great haste, they pushed off from shore. When they were at what seemed a safe distance, Ulysses shouted: "Cyclops, the gods have punished you well for your terrible deeds. Now you may know it was Ulysses who blinded you!"

In a towering rage, Polyphemus tore a huge stone from the mountainside and hurled it in the direction of the ship. The waves caused by the enormous boulder drove the ship inland and almost caused it to be swamped on the shore. His companions implored Ulysses not to taunt the giant further. So Ulysses and his men lay to their oars with all their might and soon were at a safe distance from the island.

In nine long years of war, Ulysses had never had a more narrow escape.

Pandora

THE GIFT OF THE GODS

WHEN the Earth was new, the gods on Mount Olympus decided to make a perfect creature and send their handiwork down to earth to grace and adorn the new world of Men.

They made a beautiful woman in heaven, whom they named Pandora, meaning all-gifted, for all the gods and goddesses contributed something to her making. Venus gave her beauty, Mercury gave her persuasion, Apollo gave her the gift of music—each of them gave Pandora that gift which was the most precious thing in his power to bestow.

And then the gods sent Pandora to earth. As a farewell offering, they gave her a beautiful box. They warned Pandora that under no circumstances was she to open it.

For a while, Pandora was content. Why should she not be? Everyone loved her. But Pandora, with all her great talents, was not a goddess. She was just a human being—like all of us. She wondered and wondered about what was in the beautiful box. Her curiosity grew stronger and stronger.

. . . hundreds of horrible little creatures came flying out of the box.

Finally, Pandora said to herself, "Who will know if I just take a peek into the box. I won't take anything out of it. I'll just open it a crack and close it right up again. What harm can there be in that?"

So Pandora, just like most human beings, gave in to her curiosity and disobeyed the gods. She took the box and lifted the lid, ever so slightly. Suddenly, she heard a whirring noise, and before she could do a thing, hundreds of horrible little creatures came flying out of the box.

As quickly as she could Pandora clamped down the lid again. But it was too late. In that brief moment, Pandora had released from the box all the evils and sorrows of the world. A moment before, there had been no Sickness, nor Grief; no Envy nor Cruelty—none of the things that mankind suffers today.

However, Pandora managed to close the fateful box before one thing escaped. That one thing was Hope. So even though Pandora's mischievous curiosity brought to this earth all the sorrow and pain that fills the world, we still have Hope, that most wonderful of all good things.

The Golden Touch

THE KING WHO WORSHIPPED GOLD

ONCE there dwelled in the kingdom of Phrygia, a king called Midas. On the whole he was a good king, but he had one great fault. He loved riches more than anything else in the world. He loved gold not for the good he could do with it, but for the sake of the precious metal itself. The more gold the foolish man had, the more he wanted.

But in spite of his greed for gold, King Midas was at heart a kind man. When a weary old traveler who had lost his way knocked on the great golden doors of the King's palace, Midas gave the stranger food and drink, and a place to rest his head until he was sufficiently refreshed to continue his journey.

Shortly afterward, Midas was in his treasure room admiring his stacks of gold coins and his chests of precious jewels. Suddenly he sensed that there was someone in the room with him.

Who could it be? As usual all the doors to the treasure room were triple-locked, and King Midas had given strict orders that no man was to be permitted in the treasure chamber.

The King looked up. The stranger in the room with him was no ordinary mortal. Midas recognized him as the god Bacchus, come down from Mount Olympus.

The king's mouth dropped open in surprise. Imagine seeing one of the gods in his counting room!

Bacchus spoke. "Midas," he said, "you have shown great kindness to a weary stranger who came to your door. The stranger you befriended was Silenus, my foster-father. The gods do not forget such kindnesses. What is your fondest wish? Ask, and it shall be granted!"

Midas could hardly believe his good fortune. "Gold, gold!" he thought to himself. "I shall ask for gold. More gold than any mortal man has ever seen!"

Then the king spoke, "Oh, Bacchus, my lord, grant that anything I touch shall turn to gold!"

"You have made a poor choice," said Bacchus, "but if that is what you want, I must keep my promise and grant you your wish."

King Midas was overjoyed. Poor choice, Bacchus had said. Poor choice! Nonsense! How could anything to do with gold be poor? Midas rushed out into his garden. He must see if it was really true— if he really had the golden touch. He snapped a twig from a tree and laughed with glee as he saw it turn to gold in his hand. He plucked an apple from a bough. Oh, joy! In his hand he held a perfect golden apple!

He rushed into his palace and ran from chair to chair. At his

His teeth grated on something as hard as stone.

touch, they turned to gold. His excitement knew no bounds.

He sat down to the table, laden with delectable foods and wines. He raised a morsel of food to his mouth and took a bite. His teeth grated on something as hard as stone. What was the matter? Taking the hard substance from his mouth, he saw that it was a piece of gold.

In sudden fear, he plucked a luscious grape from a platter. In horror, he saw that its lush purple ripeness had changed to hard glittering gold.

Now he realized what Bacchus had meant when he said, "You have made a poor choice."

Poor indeed was Midas! Of what use was all his gold? He could not eat gold. Too late he realized that many things other than gold are precious.

Humbly, Midas prayed to Bacchus to take back the hated gift. The god took pity on him.

"Go to the River Pactolus and plunge into its waters," Bacchus told him. "Thus you shall be cleansed of the golden touch. Perhaps then, too, you will be cleansed of your greed."

Midas quickly did as he was told and came out of the stream a changed man. No longer did riches and pomp mean everything to him. He gave much of his wealth away to the poor. He went to live in the country. There he lived simply and enjoyed as he never did before, a modest way of life—a simple life in which people were judged, not by their wealth, but by their goodness.

The Gordian Knot

THE DESTINY OF ALEXANDER

MANY hundreds of years ago there once lay in the western part of Asia a sleepy little kingdom named Phrygia. Far off the beaten track, Phrygia was neither important for its commerce nor for its culture nor for its military might. Nevertheless, the tiny kingdom had become famous throughout the world.

Phrygia's fame rested on a humble wagon that stood in the Temple of Jupiter. This wagon had been made fast to a wooden yoke with such a marvelous knot that for over a hundred years no one had been able to untie it. It was called the *Gordian Knot* because it had been tied by Gordius, the first king of Phrygia.

The oracles of the temple — those priests who were believed to have the power to foresee the future — had made a fateful prophecy:

"Whosoever undoes this wonderful work
shall have the world for his kingdom."

This promise had attracted many kings and princes and warriors to Phrygia. Each, hoping he might be the one chosen to rule the world, tried to untie the knot. But in the thousands of attempts

"It is thus," cried Alexander, *"that I unravel all Gordian Knots!"*

made in the space of a full hundred years, no one had even been able to unravel a single cord.

One day, word came that young King Alexander of Macedonia was coming to visit Phrygia. Though less than twenty-five years of age, Alexander had already conquered all of Greece and his fame had spread far and wide. Alexander was coming to grapple with the famous *Gordian Knot*.

On the fateful day, excitement was unbounded. A huge crowd filled the courtyard of the Temple of Jupiter. Young Alexander, surrounded by the notables of the city, approached the wagon.

"Is this the wondrous *Gordian Knot?*" he asked.

"The oracles have prophecied," said the elders of Phrygia, "that the man who should undo this knot would have the whole world for his kingdom."

Alexander studied the knot carefully. Then without a word, he drew his sword from its scabbard; and raising it above his head brought it down with one mighty stroke and cut the *Gordian Knot* in twain.

"It is thus," cried Alexander, "that I unravel all *Gordian Knots!*"

Alexander went on to fulfill the old prophecy. With his armies invincible he conquered nearly all of the known world. And then, the story goes, Alexander who was just over thirty years old at the time, sat down and wept, for there were no new worlds for him to conquer.

Phaeton

THE ancient Greeks imagined gods who they believed were in charge of Nature's glories. Seeing the sun rise every morning they would say, "There goes the sun-god Apollo, driving his great flaming chariot through the skies!"

Now Apollo, so the story goes, had a son on the earth, named Phaeton. The lad's mother was Clymene, a beautiful nymph. Born of such beautiful parents, Phaeton could hardly help growing up proud and handsome. It was only natural that he should become enraged when some of his young friends scoffed at his story of divine birth.

In fierce anger, Phaeton came to his mother and cried, "If I am truly the child of a god, give me some proof of it!"

"You are indeed the son of Apollo," said Clymene. "And if you wish to, you can prove it. You must journey far to the east to the land where the sun rises. There you will find Apollo. Present yourself to him and let him tell you with his own lips who you are."

The headstrong youth did not delay an instant. He set forth

at once. After many weeks journey he found himself before the glorious palace of the sun. It was so magnificent, and it gleamed so brightly that the light was almost more than he could bear.

Phaeton entered the palace. At the end of a huge hall he saw Apollo, seated on a throne which glittered with diamonds. Around the sun-god's head gleamed golden rays. On either side of the throne stood Apollo's attendants, the Hour, the Day, the Month, the Year, and the Seasons. Spring was resplendent in a garland of flowers; Summer wore a garland of grain. Autumn stood there too, in a richly colored garment, his feet stained with the juice of the grape. Winter's face was pale, his garments were dead white, and his hair and beard were stiff with frost.

Seeing Phaeton at the end of the hall, Apollo beckoned him to approach and state his errand.

"Oh light of the world!" said Phaeton. "Apollo, my father! Give me some proof, I beg you, by which I may be known as yours!"

Then Apollo recognizing his son, laid aside the beams that surrounded his head, stepped forward and embraced the handsome lad.

"Truly," he said, "you are my son and as a sign that this is so, ask for any gift you want. It shall be yours, I promise you."

Quick as a flash, Phaeton answered, "O father, then just for one day let me drive your chariot across the sky."

Apollo drew back. "Oh, my son, I have spoken rashly. Anything else in the world, I would gladly grant. You don't know what

Phaeton tried desperately to control the steeds . . .

you ask! You are a mortal, yet you ask to do what even the gods find difficult. None but myself may drive the flaming car of Day — not even Jupiter, whose terrible right hand hurls the thunderbolts. I must warn you of the terrible dangers."

"The beginning of the journey is so steep that even my fiery steeds, fresh and strong as they are in the morning, can scarcely climb it. The middle is so high that even I grow dizzy with fear when I look down at the earth and sea below. The last part of the way goes down so steeply, that it takes all my strength not to fall headlong from my chariot. And all the time the heavens are turning above my head, carrying the stars in its sweeping movement, while the earth revolves in the opposite way beneath me."

"Perhaps you think that it is all a beautiful ride with the palaces and the temples of the gods along the way. Oh, no, my son! The path is beset by fearful monsters. You must pass the horns of the Bull; draw nigh to the Lion's paws. You must pass between the claws of the Crab and the arms of the Scorpion."

"But worst of all, you have not the strength to hold in check the unruly steeds who pull the golden chariot of the sun. I can scarcely govern them myself. They are steeds born of flame, and fire breathes from their very nostrils."

"Oh my son, take back your request while you can. You came to ask for proof that I am your father? If you could look into my heart, you would see proof enough of a father's love. Phaeton, choose anything in the world, the most precious thing that sea or earth contains, and I will not refuse you. Only do not ask to ride my chariot!"

But the hot-blooded youth would not be swayed. Apollo's pleas fell on deaf ears. There was nothing for the god to do but to keep his promise. In great fear, Apollo led Phaeton to the chariot.

The boy gazed in admiration at the magnificent car. It was made of gold and silver and precious stones which reflected the brightness of the sun. Joyous and impatient to be off, Phaeton sprang into the chariot.

Apollo bathed his son's face with a powerful salve to withstand the great heat. He set the golden rays on Phaeton's head and proffered him these last words of advice. "Hold the reins tight. Do not use the whip, for the horses go fast enough of their own will. The important thing is to hold them in. Keep in the middle zone, for if you go too high, you will burn the heavenly dwellings of the gods, and if you go too low, you will set the earth on fire."

Phaeton thanked his heavy-hearted parent and seized the reins. The chariot started forward with a rush. The horses soon felt that the load they pulled was much lighter than usual. Rushing head-long as they pleased, they left Apollo's usual path. Phaeton tried desperately to control the steeds but his strength was nothing to theirs. He looked down at the earth spreading beneath him and grew pale with terror. Soon enough he wished that he had never won his request — that he had never even seen his father's flaming chariot!

The monsters of the sky stretched out their horrid claws towards him. In mortal fright, Phaeton lost his self-control. The reins dropped from his nerveless fingers. Now with no controlling hand at the reins, the horses dashed off — first high up into the heavens, then down to the earth, spreading ruin as they ran. As the chariot of the sun came close to the earth, great cities were consumed by the terrible heat; the fields of the earth were scorched and all the crops were destroyed. Mountain tops were left smoky; rivers were dried up. Destruction and terror filled the world.

Then earth in her despair cried out to Jupiter, the king of the gods, to save her. And Jupiter, seeing that not only the earth, but the heavens themselves were in danger, stood up and gathered his lightning bolts into his hand. He thundered and hurled a lightning bolt down from heaven straight toward Phaeton in his chariot. Phaeton, his hair on fire, fell headlong to the earth like a shooting star. Down he plunged to his death, into a great river.

And so Phaeton, the willful boy who thought he was mighty enough to drive the sun's own chariot, had to be destroyed so that his vanity should not result in the destruction of the world.

Echo and Narcissus

THE CHATTERING NYMPH AND THE PROUD YOUTH

IN ancient times, the fields and forests were peopled by lovely enchanted creatures called nymphs. Their homes were the trees and flowers and streams. Their food was fairy food.

Echo was one of these charming creatures. She was lovely to look at as she flitted about the forests. She might have been a perfect delight to her companions—except for one thing. Echo talked too much! Not only that, but she insisted on having the last word in every conversation.

This annoying habit finally so angered Juno, the queen of the gods that she decided to punish Echo.

"This shall be your punishment," Juno said. "You shall no longer be able to talk—with this exception: you have always insisted on having the last word; so, Echo, now you will never be able to say anything but *the last word!*"

Now in the forest where the nymphs dwelt, a handsome young man named Narcissus used to go hunting. So handsome was he, even the lovely nymphs fell in love with him at first sight. But Narcissus was terribly vain. He felt that no one was good enough to deserve his love.

One day, Echo caught sight of Narcissus and straightway fell in love with him. She yearned to tell him of her love; but because of Juno's punishment, she was powerless to speak. Echo followed Narcissus adoringly wherever he went. But now, in her affliction, Echo became very shy.

One day, while out hunting, Narcissus became separated from his companions. Hearing a sound in the woods nearby, he called out "Who's there?"

It was Echo. But all she could answer was the last word "There!"

Narcissus called again. "Come!" he said.

"Come!" replied Echo.

Still seeing no one, Narcissus cried, "Why do you shun me?"

"Shun me!" came back the reply.

"Let us join each other," called Narcissus.

Then Echo, full of love, stepped out from between the trees.

"Each other!" she said, giving Narcissus both her hands.

But Narcissus drew back in his pride. "Go away," he said. "How can you be so forward! I would rather die than that you should have me."

"Have me," wept Echo.

But in his cold pride Narcissus left her.

Echo was heartbroken. From then on, she pined away. Echo

grew thinner and thinner. Finally, nothing was left of her—but her voice.

Echo still lives among the rocks and caves of the mountains where she answers anyone who calls her. But she answers with only the last word.

But cruel Narcissus did not escape punishment. He continued in his vain self-love until such a day when he spurned another nymph who sought his affection. The hurt creature in her anguish entreated the Goddess of Love:

"Oh, goddess," she prayed, "make this hard-hearted young man know what it is to love someone who does not return his love. Let him feel the pain I now suffer."

The nymph's prayer was heard. In the middle of the forest, there was a clear fountain. Here Narcissus wandered one day; and bending over to drink, he caught sight of his own reflection in the water. He thought he saw a beautiful water nymph. Gazing in admiration, Narcissus fell in love with himself!

He stretched out his arms to clasp the beautiful being he saw in the water. The creature stretched out its arms, too. Narcissus plunged his arms into the water to embrace his beloved. Instantly, the water shivered into a thousand ripples and the creature disappeared.

A few moments later his beloved reappeared. Now Narcissus brought his lips near to the water to take a kiss. Again the image fled!

He begged his adored one to stay.

. . . bending over to drink, he caught sight of his own reflection . . .

"Why do you shun me?" he cried. "I am not ugly. The nymphs love me. Even you look at me lovingly. When I stretch out my arms, you do the same. When I blow you kisses, you answer them."

His tears fell into the water and the image began to disappear.

"Stay, I implore you!" he begged. "If I may not touch you, at least let me look at you."

Narcissus would not leave the pool. Now he knew the pain of loving in vain. Gradually, he grew pale and faded away. As he pined in hopeless love, he lost his beauty. The nymph Echo hovered near him and sorrowed for him. And when he murmured, "Alas, alas!" she answered, "Alas!"

Finally, he died of grief. The nymphs prepared to bury him. But when they came for him, he was nowhere to be found. In his stead, bending over the pool, they found a beautiful flower.

And to this day, this lovely flower grows near the water and is called the narcissus.

The Sword of Damocles

THE MAN WHO WOULD BE KING

THERE was once a rich and powerful king in Greece named Dionysius. A clever, ruthless man, Dionysius had fought his way to the throne, winning out over many other claimants. But though he gained the crown, Dionysius had made many powerful and bitter enemies in his struggle for that prize. Yet there were many who envied Dionysius and wished they were in his place.

Amongst the king's courtiers was a man called Damocles. Damocles was constantly praising Dionysius and saying, "Oh great king, you are indeed blessed of the Gods. Everything you could wish for is yours. How happy you must be!"

One day, when Damocles was speaking in his flattering way, Dionysius said, "How now, Damocles, what say you? Would you like to be king in my stead?"

Damocles was frightened, for he did not want the king to think that he was plotting to seize the throne. Quickly he replied, "Oh no, great king, I would not be king. I was only thinking how wonderful it would be to enjoy your riches for even one day."

Just above his head was an enormous sword ...

"It shall be as you desire," said King Dionysius. "For one day, you shall enjoy the position and power and luxury of a king. You shall know exactly what it feels like to be in my place."

The next day the astonished Damocles was led into the king's chamber. He was dressed in royal robes and told that he could do whatever he wished.

He ordered delicious wines and viands to be served to him. He commanded singers and dancers to amuse him, and he prepared to enjoy every luxury.

Suddenly, as he leaned back among his silken cushions, he gasped with horror. Just above his head was an enormous sword hanging by a slender thread! If the thread broke, the sword would instantly fall and kill him. He sat, pale and trembling. Pointing to the sword in terror, he whispered, "That sword! That sword! Why is that sword hanging above me? Hanging by so slender a thread?"

"I promised you," answered Dionysius, "that you should know exactly how it feels to live like a king, and now you know! Did you expect that you might enjoy all of a king's riches for nothing? Do you not know that I always live with a sword hanging over my head? I must be on my guard every moment lest I be slain."

Then Damocles answered, "O king, take back your wealth and your power! I would not have it for another moment. I would rather be a poor peasant living in a mountain hut than live in fear and trembling all the days of my life!"

Never again did Damocles envy the king.

Atalanta's Race

A CONTEST FOR LOVE OR DEATH

ONE of the loveliest maidens in the Greece of long ago was a girl named Atalanta. Many were the handsome suitors who sought her hand. But Atalanta was simply not interested in any of them, or even in the idea of marriage.

The young men, however, were not easily discouraged. They constantly urged her to listen to their pleas.

Finally she hit upon a scheme to discourage her suitors. She gathered them all together and said, "Whoever wants to marry me must run a race with me. If he wins, I will marry him. But if he loses, he must pay for his loss with his life!"

Atalanta's strange proposal had the desired effect with most of her young men. Besides her beauty, Atalanta was renowned throughout Greece for her prowess in sports. It was said that she was the swiftest runner in the world — that she could outrun anyone except Mercury, the fleet messenger of the gods.

But there still remained a few young men so smitten with Atalanta that they were willing to gamble their lives against such overwhelming odds. So a time for the race was set.

Hippomenes, a young man who had never seen Atalanta, was chosen to be judge. When he learned the conditions of the race, he was astounded. "How could any girl be worth such a risk?" he wondered.

But on the day of the race, when Hippomenes saw the fair Atalanta, he too fell in love with her!

The race began. Hippomenes watched, his heart pounding with fear, lest one of the young men win the race and carry off the beautiful prize. But they were all far behind Atalanta as she flew across the finish line. One and all, the young men had to pay with their lives for their reckless ardor.

But Hippomenes, whose heart now was hopelessly lost to Atalanta, was not daunted by the dreadful fate of the others. He came to Atalanta and said, "Fair maid, I would try for your hand."

Atalanta looked at him pityingly. How could she let this handsome young man throw his life away? She tried to discourage Hippomenes. "You have seen what happened to the others. You see how fleet of foot I am. Do not try to race against me. You will surely lose the race and your life with it."

But Hippomenes would not be put off. He insisted that Atalanta keep to her terms.

Hippomenes prayed to Venus, the goddess of Love. "Oh, Venus," he prayed, "whatever aid you can give me, grant it now, for if I love so deeply it must be that you have willed it so."

Venus heard his prayer. Just as the race was about to begin, three golden apples appeared in Hippomenes' hand. They could only have come from Venus' own garden. As Hippomenes looked at the apples in amazement, a soft voice whispered in his ear, "Race well, Hippomenes. And if you have the wit to use these golden apples correctly, they will win the race for you."

Atalanta and Hippomenes moved to the starting line. The watching crowds were impatient for the race to begin. The signal was given and off they went.

At first Hippomenes, no mean runner himself, kept pace with Atalanta. But soon the maiden, darting forward as gracefully as a bird, began to draw away from him. Her feet scarcely seemed to touch the ground so swiftly did she run.

The spectators were all hoping for Hippomenes to win. "Faster! Faster!" they cried. But the young man's throat was dry — his stout heart felt as though it were going to burst within him. Try as he might, the maiden kept ahead of him, running easily.

Then Hippomenes remembered the gift of Venus. He threw one of the golden apples so that it landed near Atalanta's twinkling feet. Atalanta was entranced by it. "What is that beautiful shining thing?" she wondered. She stopped to pick up the apple, and while she paused Hippomenes raced past her.

Atalanta was not alarmed. She knew that she could easily catch up to Hippomenes and go on past him. Besides she was beginning to feel sorry for the handsome young man. "He is so young to die,"

She stopped to pick up the apple . . .

she thought. "It is not because he is handsome and bold that I pity him; it is only because he is so young."

But Atalanta straightened up, and with the apple in her hand, sped after Hippomenes. In a moment she had caught up with him again, and in a few more strides she was leaving him behind.

Again Hippomenes flung a golden apple ahead of Atalanta. The maiden stopped to scoop it up. Once again, Hippomenes raced past her. But it did not take long for Atalanta to close the distance between them and draw far ahead once more.

The goal came into sight and the spectators held their breath. There seemed to be no hope for the brave young man.

Hippomenes' lungs seemed to be bursting within him. Gasping for breath, he hurled the last apple. This time he tossed it off to one side. Atalanta, running after it, left the path to pursue the apple. Now Hippomenes made a final desperate effort. With a last burst of strength he threw himself forward and sped over the goal, a scant step ahead of the flying girl.

So with the help of Venus, goddess of Love, Hippomenes won the lovely Atalanta. But Atalanta was not unhappy. She knew that though she had lost the race, she had won true love.

Prometheus

THE GIVER OF FIRE

THE old Greek legends tell us that first the gods made the earth. Then they gave the task of creating the creatures of the earth to two giants. One was named Prometheus, which means Forethought, and the other was named Epimetheus, which means Afterthought.

The giants were well named. Epimetheus gave special gifts to all the animals. He gave powerful wings to the eagle, great strength and courage to the lion, and cunning to the fox; but when it came time to provide for Man, he had nothing special left to give him. He had not thought of that in time.

Then Prometheus spoke: "Man is to be superior to all living things on earth. How can we make him thus? We must give him a very special gift. But you and I have nothing left to give, so we must take our gift from the gods."

Then Prometheus went up to heaven, the home of the gods, and, stealing into the palace of the Sun, made off with a brand of fire and brought it back to earth. This was his gift to man.

There Prometheus was forced to lie, while vultures gnawed . . .

And he said, "With fire, you will be able to make weapons; and with weapons in your hands, you can overcome the fiercest and strongest animals.

"With fire, you will be able to make tools to cultivate the earth, and thus you will always have food to sustain yourselves.

"You will be able to build strong houses to shelter you from the weather, and fire will warm your homes for you and keep you alive in the bitterest cold.

"Fire shall make you the mightiest creature on earth!"

The gift was a great one, indeed. But for his kindness in giving this gift to Man, Prometheus paid a heavy price. For Jupiter, the king of the gods, was so enraged when he discovered that the gods' secret had been stolen, that he had Prometheus chained to a rock on the top of a mountain, in punishment for his deed. There Prometheus was forced to lie, while vultures gnawed perpetually at his insides; for no matter how long the birds tore at his vitals, they never completely consumed them.

For hundreds of years, Prometheus lay like this, too proud to ask Jupiter for mercy, until Hercules, the hero who was half man and half god, broke Prometheus' chains and released him from his agony, at last.

Arachne

THE STORY OF THE SPIDER

THE maiden, Arachne, was so skillful at weaving and embroidery that people would come from far and near to marvel at her work.

Not only was the work itself beautiful, but Arachne's movements as she wove were so graceful and lovely that people would say, "Minerva herself must have taught you!"

But Arachne had become so conceited and vain of her skill that she could not bear to hear even the goddess Minerva praised.

"Is that so," scoffed Arachne. "Let Minerva try her skill with me. If I do not surpass her, I will pay the penalty!"

Then Minerva, hearing this, was angry. But in her greatness she was still merciful. She disguised herself as an old woman and came to Arachne.

"I am an old woman," she said, "and I have learned much in my long lifetime. Challenge your fellow mortals, if you will, but do not challenge a goddess. If I were you, I would beg Minerva's forgiveness for your words, and hope that she will pardon you."

. . . she touched Arachne's forehead and made her feel her guilt . . .

But Arachne laughed scornfully.

"I am not afraid," she said. "I meant what I said. Let Minerva come down and compete with me, if she dares!"

"She comes!" answered Minerva; and dropping her disguise, she stepped forward.

Arachne paled, but only for a moment. "Let us begin," she said.

The contest began. Minerva wove scenes showing the immense power of the gods. The beauty of her work was so great that the watchers were breathless with admiration.

Then Arachne began to weave. She purposely chose to weave pictures showing the weaknesses and errors of the gods. Her pictures were so lifelike they almost seemed to move. She wove so marvelously that even Minerva herself could not help but admire Arachne's art. And, furious at Arachne's insult, Minerva struck her shuttle, and it fell to pieces. Then she touched Arachne's forehead and made her feel her guilt and shame.

Arachne, in remorse, rushed away and hung herself. Then Minerva took some pity on her and said, "Live, guilty woman. But from now on you and your children shall continue to hang."

As she spoke, Arachne's form shriveled up, while her arms and legs grew larger, until finally she was changed into a spider. Her descendants can be seen to this day, hanging from the thread which they weave into a web.

The Return of Ulysses

A KING METES OUT JUSTICE

WHEN Ulysses had set forth for Troy to help the Greeks in their war, he was a young man. He had found it hard to part from his beautiful wife, Penelope, and his baby son, Telemachus. Even so, he thought that at most a year or so would pass before he could return.

But it took nine years to win the Trojan War. And because Ulysses had angered certain gods, he was forced to wander for eleven more years before he finally reached his home.

During the twenty long years that Ulysses was gone, Penelope had remained faithful to him. She did her best to order well the affairs of their kingdom. But after a while, the neighboring princes, as well as the men of her own court, convinced that Ulysses would never return, pressed her to choose one of them for a husband, to be king of Ithaca.

For a long time, Penelope put them off. The suitors became more and more insistent. They lorded it over the palace and the people, as if they were the rulers already. Penelope was helpless to hold them in check. They made the palace and the country poor with their spendthrift ways. Things got so bad that Penelope, fearful for her son's life, sent him away. He searched for his father, but in vain.

Meanwhile, the suitors were angry that Penelope did not make her choice. For years, she had put them off, saying that when she had finished a certain piece of tapestry which she was weaving on her loom, she would choose a husband from among them. In the daytime she wove, but at night she secretly unraveled her work. Finally, however, the suitors would wait no longer.

Things were in this state when Ulysses, having lost all his men and ships, landed alone in his city. Minerva, the goddess of Wisdom, who favored Ulysses, knew that the wicked suitors would be far from glad to see Ulysses return. They had wanted his kingdom for too long to allow him to recover it. They would surely kill him.

So Minerva changed Ulysses into an old beggar. While in this disguise, he met an old swineherd named Emmaeus who had been a faithful servant of Ulysses during all the long years of his absence. Emmaeus did not know who the old beggar was, but he received him kindly.

Minerva also advised Ulysses' son, Telemachus, who was now a young man, to return to his country. Telemachus, knowing that his own life was in danger from the suitors, first went to the hut of Emmaeus. He sent Emmaeus to his mother at the palace to tell her of his arrival.

While Emmaeus was gone, Ulysses told his son who he really

was. At that, Minerva restored to Ulysses his own manly good looks, but he kept the clothes of a beggar.

Telemachus wept with joy to see his father, for whom he had yearned so many years. One can imagine Ulysses' feelings to be at last holding his son in his arms.

They took counsel together as to how they should overcome the powerful suitors who had taken over their kingdom, and how they would punish them.

They made a plan. Telemachus and Ulysses went to the palace —Telemachus, as the young prince coming home, and Ulysses disguised as an old beggar, a sort of wandering storyteller.

In the palace hall, they found the usual scene of riotous feasting. The suitors pretended to greet Telemachus with joy, but they were furious that their plots to kill him had gone awry.

As Ulysses entered the courtyard of his palace, unrecognized even by his wife, his old dog, Argus, was lying in the yard. Argus had been too weak to move, but suddenly he raised his head, his ears stood up, and he was all joy, for he knew his master. Lucky for Ulysses that few people were around to see this sight!

This was the day, however, when Penelope had finally been forced to promise to choose a husband. The suitors were to contest for her hand by a trial of skill with the bow and arrow. Twelve rings were set up against the wall. The man who succeeded in shooting an arrow into every one of the twelve rings was to have the queen as his bride.

"Now for another mark!"

There was an old bow in the palace armory which had belonged to Ulysses. This bow was to be used in the contest. Telemachus, in accordance with the plans he had made with Ulysses, allowed only this weapon to be brought into the hall. His excuse was that, in the heat of the contest, fighting might break out amongst the suitors.

They got ready for the contest, but when they tried to bend the old bow to attach the string, no one could do it. First Telemachus, then each of the suitors in turn tried to bend the bow, but without success.

Then Ulysses spoke up. "Let me try," he said. "Beggar though I am, I was once a soldier, and maybe there is some strength left in my limbs."

The suitors were furious at his insolence. They wanted the beggar thrown out.

But Telemachus calmed them. He pretended that it would be amusing to watch the beggar struggle, and he handed the bow to Ulysses.

Then Ulysses, with great ease, fitted the string to the bow. While everyone watched in astonishment, he shot twelve arrows, one after another, into the twelve rings.

Then he fitted another arrow to his bow. "Now for another mark!" he said. And with that, he aimed for the most overbearing of all the suitors. The arrow pierced the man's throat, and he died instantly.

Now Telemachus, Emmaeus, and another faithful follower

sprang to arms. The suitors rushed for their weapons, but the doors had been locked by Emmaeus, and they were helpless.

Ulysses now told them that he was the king whose land they had invaded, whose riches they had spent, whose wife and son they had persecuted for so many years. They were all killed, and Ulysses was once more king in his own land.

Circe, the Enchantress

A SORCERESS IS OUTWITTED

ULYSSES, by his cleverness and courage, escaped from the giant Cyclops, but soon other dangers beset him and his men.

They sailed on toward home, but once more it was necessary to land and refill their water casks. They came to a beautiful island. Ulysses climbed a high hill near the shore and looked about him. In the distance, he saw a palace surrounded by groves of trees.

He sent one-half of his crew, with Eurylochus in charge, to the palace to find out if they would be received with kindness.

Eurylochus and the men approached the palace cautiously. Suddenly, they found themselves surrounded by lions, tigers, wolves, and all sorts of fierce-looking animals. They stood, transfixed with fear. But the animals did not attack them. Quite the contrary, they seemed completely tamed and walked quietly amongst the men.

The men did not know it, but they had wandered into the kingdom of Circe, the enchantress. These animals had once been men, but they had been changed into beasts by Circe!

At that very moment, the men heard a lovely voice singing. Not realizing the terrible danger they were in, they pressed forward.

The singing stopped, and Circe, the beautiful but wicked sorceress, came out to greet them. Sweetly, she asked them to come in to rest and refresh themselves. The men hurried forward, delighted with their welcome. All but Eurylochus, their wise leader. Something did not seem right to him. His suspicions were aroused, and he did not enter the palace but stood where he could look in and watch what was happening.

Circe had delicious food spread before the men. Jars of wine were served to them. The men ate and drank hungrily. That was just what Circe wanted, for the food was enchanted. When Circe saw that they had eaten and drunk their fill, she touched each one with her wand.

Instantly, they were changed into swine. These men, who, a moment before, were stalwart seamen, now had the snouts and ugly, bristly forms of pigs. They could not talk; they could only grunt. But their minds and feelings were still those of the men they had been.

In contempt and derision, Circe shut them in sties and gave them acorns to eat.

Eurylochus, horrified at what he had seen, rushed back to the ship. He told Ulysses what had happened.

When Ulysses heard the fearful report, he determined to go to the men's aid and deliver them from Circe's sorceries.

As he strode forward, a handsome youth stopped him. It was

Instantly, they were changed into swine.

none other than the god, Mercury, who had come to warn him of Circe's arts and enchantments. When he saw that Ulysses insisted on trying to rescue his men, he gave him a sprig of a plant. This was a magic plant, and it would save Ulysses from Circe's enchantments.

When Ulysses reached the palace, Circe, sure that she had another victim in her power, greeted him cordially. She gave him food and drink, and then, touching him with her wand, she cried, "Hence! Seek thy sty and wallow with thy friends!"

But Ulysses drew his sword and rushed upon the wicked Circe. She fell on her knees and begged for mercy.

"Where are my friends?" asked Ulysses. "Restore them to their human forms, if you do not wish to die!"

He made Circe promise that she would not harm him or his companions, and that she would give them everything they needed.

His men were changed back into their original forms. The rest of the men from Ulysses' ship were sent for, and all were feasted and magnificently entertained by Circe.

When the time came for them to leave, Circe, now completely their friend, did them a service without which they would have all lost their lives.

In order to pass Circe's island, they would have to pass the Island of the Sirens. These Sirens were sea nymphs who sang so beautifully that no one could resist them. When passing seamen heard their singing, they could not bear to leave them. The men would cast themselves into the sea to reach them, and would be drowned.

Circe told Ulysses to fill his sailors' ears with wax, before they approached within sound of the Sirens. He himself should instruct his men to tie him securely to the mast and not to release him from his bonds until they had passed the Sirens. Ulysses did as Circe had told him.

Soon, they drew near the Island of the Sirens. Over the water came the sound of their singing, so sweet, so utterly ravishing, that Ulysses could not stand it. He forgot everything in the world, only that he must go to them. He begged, he wept, and he stormed, demanding that his men untie him. But they, who could not hear the singing of the Sirens, remembered what he had told them. The more he implored, the tighter they tied his cords, and the faster they rowed.

Gradually, the fatal music grew fainter. When Ulysses could hear it no more, and they were safely past the danger, he signaled his men to remove the wax from their ears. Then they untied him. Ulysses thanked them for their faithfulness to him, and they went on their way.

Damon and Pythias

THE MOST FAITHFUL OF FRIENDS

MORE than two thousand years ago, on the island of Sicily, there lived two young men named Damon and Pythias. Damon and Pythias were famed far and wide for their great friendship. Indeed, their names have come down to us to this day, as symbols of what true friendship means.

Syracuse, the city in which they lived, was ruled by a cruel and tyrannical king, named Dionysius. Dionysius cared nothing about his people. His laws were harsh and brutal, and he enforced them pitilessly. But dreadful as were the hardships the people were forced to endure, they did not rebel for fear of the king's great and powerful army. No one even dared to complain, because anyone who was caught saying anything against the king was immediately punished.

But Damon and Pythias were brave men and refused to keep silent about the cruelties of their ruler. One day, one of the King's soldiers overheard Pythias talking against Dionysius. He immediately arrested him and brought him before the king. But brave Pythias was not frightened. His hatred of Dionysius was so great that he fearlessly told him to his face that he was a cruel and wicked tyrant! When Dionysius heard this, he became so furious that he had Pythias put in chains and thrown into prison immediately. He declared that in two weeks' time, Pythias would die.

When Damon discovered what had happened to his friend, he was heartbroken. He rushed to the prison to see Pythias. When he was brought before him, he said, "Oh, my dear friend, if only I could save you. I would willingly die myself, that you might live!"

Then Pythias answered, "I know that nothing can save me, and I am prepared to die. But there is one thought that torments me — what will happen to my sister and my old mother, when I am gone? If only I could go to see them before I die; if only I had a chance to make arrangements to take care of them, so they will not starve when I am no longer here!"

Then Damon went to the King and begged him to allow Pythias to go to see his mother before he died. "I will take his place in prison," he said, "until he comes back. If he is not here on the day of execution, kill me instead of him!"

Dionysius was astonished at this request. Never before had he seen or heard of anything like it. It so aroused his amazement and curiosity, that despite his anger at Pythias he agreed to it. "But," he said to Damon, "I warn you, if your friend does not return on time, I will not spare your life!"

Damon went to his friend Pythias to tell him of his bargain with the king. Then Pythias set out to see his mother, and Damon was put in his place in prison.

More than a week went by. The day for the execution drew near and Pythias had not yet returned. "You see," said Dionysius, "your friend has tricked you. He will not come back here to be killed. You were a fool to take his place! He has run away and left you here to die instead of him."

But Damon's faith in his friend did not waver. "I know Pythias will return," he said, "and I am not afraid."

And indeed his faith was justified. Pythias had gone home and made arrangements so that his mother and sister would be able to live comfortably for many years. Then he had said a last farewell to his family, and set out to return to Syracuse. But the way back was not easy. Robbers set upon him and stole his money. Then they tied him to a tree and left him there. No entreaty of his could make them set him free. At last, after a desperate struggle, he managed to break his bonds. Then he set off once more, as fast as possible, to reach Syracuse; for time was getting short. Day and night, he travelled, without stopping. Hungry and exhausted, he stumbled through forests, swam across rivers, and crawled through swamps, in a desperate effort to get to Syracuse in time to save Damon's life.

But the day of the execution dawned and Pythias had not yet returned.

"Ha," sneered Dionysius, as Damon was being led into the prison courtyard for his execution. "Tell me, I pray you, where is your dear friend now?"

. . . a pale, breathless man rushed into the courtyard.

But Damon said, "If he has not come, I know it is through no fault of his own. I am glad to die in his place!"

Just as Damon finished saying these words, a pale, breathless man rushed into the courtyard. It was Pythias! Sobbing with relief, he threw his arms around Damon's neck saying, "Oh, my friend, thank God I am not too late!"

When Dionysius and his cruel soldiers saw this, even their hard hearts were moved.

"Never in all my life have I seen such faith and loyalty between friends," said Dionysius. "You may go free! I cannot destroy such a love as yours. Though I am a king and have treasure chests filled with gold and precious stones, though I rule over many people and command great armies, I would gladly give up all my money and power to have one friend like Damon or Pythias!"

Proserpine and Pluto

HOW SPRINGTIME COMES TO THE EARTH

FAR down under the surface of the earth lay the lands of Pluto, god of the Underworld. Pluto, who despised light and avoided cheer, rarely left his dark and gloomy kingdom. But one day, he paid a short visit to the surface of the earth.

As he sped along the earth in his black chariot drawn by four black horses, he was seen by Cupid.

"What great good luck!" thought the mischievous god of Love, as he fitted an arrow to his bow. "Here's a target I may never get a chance at again!"

Cupid took careful aim and shot his arrow straight into Pluto's heart.

Now anyone who is hit by Cupid's arrow doesn't die, but, instead, falls in love with the first person he sees. The first person Pluto saw was Proserpine, the lovely daughter of Ceres, goddess of the Harvest. Proserpine was gathering lilies beside a gay, bubbling stream. When Pluto saw her, he was overwhelmed with love. He swept Proserpine up in his arms and carried her off in his chariot. The terrified girl screamed for help, but there was no one to hear her cries.

Pluto struck the earth with his great three-pronged spear, and the ground opened up. Into the opening, Pluto drove his plunging black horses. The earth closed again, while down, down, deep into the earth the chariot sped with Pluto and his beautiful prisoner.

Soon they arrived at Pluto's palace. The Underworld king spoke words of love to Proserpine. He begged her not to be afraid. "You shall be my beloved," he said. "You shall reign as queen over all the realms of the dead."

But Proserpine only shook her head and wept. She would not look at Pluto; she would neither eat nor drink.

Far away, on the surface of the earth, Proserpine's mother, Ceres, was enveloped in despair. She searched the world over for her missing daughter, but she could not find her.

One day, weary and sad, Ceres sat down beside a river. The place she chose to rest was a fateful one. It was the very spot where Pluto had caused the earth to open, so that he could pass in with Proserpine!

The nymph who lived in the nearby river had seen everything that happened. She was terribly afraid of Pluto, and dared not tell Ceres. Instead, she lifted up the sash which Proserpine had dropped, and wafted it to the feet of her mother.

Ceres cried out with grief at the sight of her daughter's sash. Now she knew that Proserpine was in the earth, but she did not know what had happened. In her grief and anger, she blamed the earth itself.

At the end of six months, Proserpine comes back to her mother.

"Ungrateful soil!" cried Ceres. "I have given you richness and clothed you with greenery and nourishing grain. Is this how you repay me? Now no more shall you enjoy my favors."

In her anger, Ceres sent too much rain, which killed the crops; then too much sun, which dried the fields. The leaves fell from the trees, cattle died, and ploughs broke in the furrows. The poor earth suffered terribly.

Finally, Arethusa, the nymph, interceded for the land. "Goddess," she said, "do not blame the land. Unwillingly did it open to let your daughter in. Pluto carried her off to be queen of the Underworld. As my waters seeped through the earth, they saw her there. She is sad, but she is not afraid."

When Ceres heard this, she determined to get help. She quickly turned her chariot toward heaven and threw herself before the throne of Jupiter, the king of the gods. She begged him to bring Proserpine back to the earth—to force Pluto to give up her daughter.

Jupiter consented, but he was forced to make one condition. If Proserpine had not eaten anything while in the Underworld she could return; otherwise, she must stay in Pluto's kingdom.

Mercury, the messenger of the gods, was then sent to Pluto with Jupiter's orders to return Proserpine to her mother.

Pluto could not refuse an order from Jupiter. But first, the clever Pluto offered Proserpine a pomegranate. No longer afraid of Pluto, Proserpine started to bite into the fruit. In alarm, Mercury stopped her—but not before she had swallowed six pomegranate seeds. Now,

Pluto was able to demand that Proserpine spend six months of the year with him—one month for each seed she had swallowed.

So it was arranged. For six months each year, Proserpine must leave her mother, Ceres, and be Pluto's queen. During that time, Ceres is sad and unconcerned with the earth. Everything dies. It is winter.

At the end of six months, Proserpine comes back to her mother. She brings joy to Ceres and bright springtime to the earth.

Cupid and Psyche

THE IMMORTAL LOVERS

LONG ago, there lived a king who had three daughters. Two of them were very pretty, but the youngest was the most beautiful one of all. Her name was Psyche.

She was so beautiful that her fame spread. People came from far and near just to see her. Many people thought she must be a goddess, and they scattered flowers in her path and worshiped her.

When Venus, the goddess of Love and Beauty, saw this, she was very angry.

"Shall a mortal girl take away from me my homage and honor?" she cried.

Then turning to her son, Cupid, she said, "If you honor your mother you will do as I say. Go now to earth and strike Psyche with one of your arrows and cause her to fall in love with the most unworthy of men. That shall be her punishment."

Cupid set forth to do his mother's bidding. He carried with him two jars from his mother's garden. One contained bitter water, which brought sadness, and the other, sweet water, which brought

102

joy. When he came to Psyche's room, where she was sleeping, he sprinkled a few drops of the bitter water over her lips.

Psyche opened her lovely eyes. At the sight of them, Cupid became so confused that he wounded himself with his own arrow. Now he was stricken with a deep love for her. Quickly, he tried to undo the harm he had done her, and sprinkled the sweet water of joy over her. Then he fled. Psyche did not see him, for he had made himself invisible. But Cupid had not only seen Psyche, he had pierced himself with his own arrow of love. From now on, he would love no one but her.

His mother had sent him to punish Psyche. Now he had fallen in love with her. His mother's anger would be terrible if she found out. What could he do? He had to flee from the sight of his beloved Psyche.

From then on, however, Psyche derived no joy from her beauty. For Venus, in her jealousy, made it so that no one came forth to ask Psyche in marriage. Her two sisters were married to kings, but Psyche grew lonelier every day.

As time went on, her father and mother, saddened at the unhappiness of their beloved daughter, felt that they must do something to help her. They consulted an oracle and asked for advice. The oracle told them that Psyche would marry no ordinary mortal, but a monster whom no one could resist. This monster was waiting for her on top of a high mountain.

The dreadful decree of the fortuneteller filled the king and queen with grief. But Psyche said, "Why are you all so sad now? You should have been sad when people showered me with honor and called me as lovely as Venus; for now I see that because of this, I am suffering this cruel fate. As for me, my life is so lonely, I care not what happens to me. Take me to the mountain."

So, amid weeping and sorrow, Psyche was led to the top of the mountain and left there alone.

As Psyche stood there, expecting the worst, a gentle breeze suddenly lifted her up and carried her away. Softly, it set her down in a beautiful valley. She could not understand what was happening, but, worn out from all her fears, she fell asleep.

When she awoke, she looked around her and found herself on the grounds of a magnificent palace. As she gazed in amazement, a voice spoke to her, saying, "Queenly lady, all that you see is yours. We are your servants and shall obey all your commands. Your room awaits you, with a bed of down. Rest yourself. Then, when you wish to eat, supper will await you."

Psyche did as the voice told her. After she had bathed and rested, she sat down in the dining alcove, where a table appeared as if from nowhere, laden with the choicest foods and wines. Soft music played for her while she ate.

When night came, her husband came to her. She could not see him, for it was dark, but he spoke to her with such tender words that she could not help but love him. Then, before dawn, he left her.

All day, she yearned for his return, and, with the darkness, he came back to her. She begged him to stay, to let her see him, but he would not consent.

"Do not try to see me," he said. "Why should you wish to see me? Do you doubt my love? If you saw me, maybe you would fear me, maybe you would adore me as a god. I would rather that you loved me as an equal than adored me as a god."

Psyche was calmed by these words. She was content, for she loved her husband, and she loved her beautiful palace. But after a while, she grew lonely for her parents and her sisters. She knew that they thought she had been carried off by a monster, yet here she was, safe and sound. If she could only let them know. If she could only see them!

When her husband came at night, she poured out her sorrow to him, and finally, with a heavy heart, he agreed to let her two sisters visit her.

The same gentle breeze carried them to her. Psyche was over-joyed to see them. She greeted them with kisses and showered them with gifts.

When her sisters saw the beautiful palace that Psyche lived in, full of priceless treasures so much richer than theirs, they became envious of her good fortune. They asked her all sorts of questions, especially about her husband.

"Where is he?" they asked. "Why do we not see him?"

At first, Psyche tried to pretend that he was temporarily away from home. But finally, she confessed the truth—that she had never seen him, that he only came to her at night.

"O, Psyche!" they cried. "Do not be deceived. Remember the oracle's prophecy, that you would be carried off by a monster. You have never seen your husband. Why does he hide himself from you? It stands to reason that he means to harm you. Very likely he means to fatten you just to eat you up.

"You must do as we say. Prepare for yourself a lamp and a sharp knife. When he comes to you at night, wait 'til he has fallen asleep. Then light your lamp and look at him. You will see for yourself whether he is a monster. If he is, quickly cut off his head, and free yourself from his imprisonment."

Psyche would not listen to such ideas. She insisted that her husband loved her, and that he was not what they said. But after they returned home, their words began to torment her. Could they be right?

Finally, her curiosity and fears got the better of her, and she prepared the lamp and the knife. That night, when her husband had fallen asleep, she got up quietly and brought the lamp over to the couch where he lay.

As the lamp lit up the couch, she saw, not an ugly monster, but the most beautiful and charming of the gods.

His golden curls, his beautiful form with lovely wings on his shoulders, filled her with adoration and love. She stood transfixed, forgetting everything but her love for him. She leaned over him.

Suddenly, a drop of hot oil, from the lamp she was holding, fell on the sleeping Cupid. The burning pain awakened him.

He looked into her eyes with anger and sadness.

"Oh, Psyche," he said. "Is this how you repay me? I disobeyed my mother's commands and made you my wife. Yet you would sooner believe the words of your sisters than my acts of love. Love cannot live with suspicion. I leave you now forever."

With these words, Cupid arose and flew away.

Psyche, in despair, tried to follow him. But it was no use. Now, indeed, she was lonely. Nothing meant anything to her but her love for Cupid, and she made up her mind that she must find him and beg his forgiveness. She set forth, not really knowing where to go, but hoping that somehow she would find him.

Day and night she searched for him, without success. Then, one day, she came to a beautiful temple.

"Perhaps my lord lives in this lovely place," she thought.

As she entered the temple, she found piles of corn and barley grains in great disorder, strewn all about. Immediately, she set to work and sorted out the grains in their proper places. As she was engaged in this work, the goddess Ceres, whose temple this was, spoke to her.

"Oh Psyche," she said, "truly I pity you. I cannot help you, for Venus is angry with you. But perhaps if you go to her and try to win her favor by modesty and willingness to serve her, she will forgive you and restore your husband to you."

So Psyche, willing to do anything to win back her husband, went to the temple of Venus to do as Ceres had advised.

Venus received her with anger. "So finally you come to me, faithless girl," she cried. "Finally, you remember that I am your mistress. You are so ugly that the only way you can be worthy of your lover is by diligence and industry as a housewife. I will see what kind of a housewife you are!"

So saying, she led Psyche to a large storehouse filled with a tremendous pile of wheat, barley, millet, beans, and lentils—all mixed together.

"Separate all these grains. See that you get it done before evening," she said. And with that, she left Psyche to her task.

Psyche gazed hopelessly at the impossible task. How could she possibly succeed? What could she do?

While she sat, not knowing what to do, a little ant appeared. He had been sent by Cupid, who knew of her plight. The little ant, followed by a whole army of ants, set to work. All day long, they worked, separating each of the seeds, grain by grain.

When evening came, and Venus appeared, she was astonished to see the work accomplished.

"This is no work of yours, wicked one!" she cried. And she threw Psyche a piece of black bread for her supper.

The next morning, Venus appeared again.

"I have another task for you," she said. "See there, on the other side of the river is a flock of sheep. Their fleeces are all of pure gold. Go and bring me a sample of this golden fleece from every one of

The burning pain awakened him.

their backs." Then she left.

Psyche prepared to do as she was bid. As she stood on the bank of the rushing river, about to cross, she heard a voice speaking to her.

"Unfortunate girl," it said. "Do not try to cross the rough stream to the field where the golden sheep are grazing. For they are sheep of the sun. They are filled with a wild rage to devour mortals. Wait until they become calm, when they lie down to rest in the shade at noontime. Then you can cross the river, and you will find the woolly gold of their fleeces sticking to the bushes."

In gratitude, Psyche heeded the warning and did as she was told.

When evening came, she was ready for Venus, with her arms full of the golden wool.

Now Venus was angrier than ever, for she knew that Psyche could not have done it without help.

"I know full well that you could not have done this unaided. Therefore I am not convinced that you are a good worker. I have yet another task for you.

"Take this box to Proserpine, queen of the Underworld, and say to her, 'My mistress, Venus, desires you to send her some of your beauty, for in tending her sick son, she has lost some of her own.'"

Psyche now had no hope at all. For who ever had gone to the kingdom of the dead and returned?

Then she heard a voice speaking to her. "Two times you have been saved. Have confidence. Do what I tell you, and you will accomplish this task, too."

Then the voice told her how to escape all the dangers on the road, how to calm the three-headed dog which guards the palace of Proserpine, and how to get the ferryman to row her across the river to the dead and to bring her back again.

"But when Proserpine has filled your box with beauty, as Venus requested, do not open the box . . . under **any** circumstances!"

Psyche did as the voice directed her and made her way to Queen Proserpine. The queen fulfilled her request and gave her back the box filled with beauty.

Psyche returned from inside the earth, glad to be back under the open sky once more. However, instead of being happy at her success, she began to feel sadder than ever.

"Venus tells me I am no longer lovely. How will I ever win back my beloved husband unless I am beautiful? Of what use is all my work unless he loves me? Here is this box filled with a goddess's beauty. I will take just a little of it to help me."

So she carefully opened the box, not knowing that it contained a different sort of beauty than she imagined. To Proserpine, queen of the dead, death was a sort of beauty, and that was what she had put in the box.

The sleep of death overcame Psyche, and there on the hillside she lay motionless.

All this time, Cupid had been locked up in a room by his mother, Venus. But now, when he saw Psyche lying as if dead on the hillside, he escaped from the room where his mother had kept him prisoner, and flew to the spot where she lay. He leaned down and kissed her. His divine kiss overcame the deathly sleep, and Psyche opened her eyes.

"Oh my Psyche, once more you have almost lost everything because of your curiosity," he said. "Finish the task which my mother gave you. Bring her the box into which I have returned the sleep which overcame you. Then leave the rest to me."

Cupid flew up to the heavens. He presented himself before the throne of Jupiter himself and pleaded for Psyche's life. Jupiter was so moved by Cupid's love for Psyche that he prevailed on Venus to give her consent to their marriage.

So Psyche was carried to heaven where she was given a cup of ambrosia to drink. This made her immortal, like the gods; and so Cupid and Psyche were united forever.

The Faithful Couple

KINDNESS REWARDED

ONCE upon a time, Jupiter, the king of the gods, and his son, Mercury, were traveling on the earth disguised as ordinary mortals. To everyone, they looked like just an old man and his son.

One evening, they came to a village. They knocked on the door of a house, and asked for food and shelter.

"We are weary and hungry," they said. "Perhaps you can help us."

"It's late. Go away!" came the answer.

In such a selfish and unkind way, they were turned away from house after house.

At last they came to a little, thatch-roofed cottage outside of the town. A poor old man and his wife lived here. This old couple knew what it was to be tired and hungry. All their lives, they had worked hard. Instead of being bitter and envious of other people's wealth, they lived simply, as best they could, and sympathized with their fellow men.

To this humble house came the two gods, still in their disguises.

With kindness, the old wife, whose name was Baucis, welcomed them in.

The old man, Philemon, spread a cloth over a rickety bench, and asked them to sit down. He warmed some water for them to wash the dust of the roads off their hands. Baucis set to work immediately to prepare the best meal that she could.

It was a simple meal, not at all like the fine food that the gods usually ate. The wine was new and sour, not old and sweet, but it was the finest that the old couple had. And while the gods were waiting for the meal to be cooked, the old couple's pleasant conversation made the time pass quickly.

Then they all sat down together in a happy mood. But gradually, Baucis and Philemon began to notice something strange—the more wine they poured into the cups, the more wine there seemed to be in the pitcher. Suddenly, they realized that these were not poor travelers, but gods.

They fell on their knees and begged forgiveness that they had offered such poor hospitality to Jupiter and Mercury.

"Oh, no," said Jupiter. "You shared what was your best with humble wayfarers. You did not know who we were, yet you held back nothing from us and treated us with loving kindness. Even the gods could not do more.

"The hardhearted people of your village shall be punished, but you shall be rewarded. Come with us to the top of yonder hill."

So Baucis and Philemon climbed to the top of the hill with them.

They fell on their knees and begged forgiveness . . .

"Look," said Jupiter, "such is the fate of your village."

Baucis and Philemon looked down on the valley, and where once was their village, now there was a huge lake. All the houses except their humble cottage were sunk beneath the water.

As they watched, their cottage was transformed into a beautiful temple. The straw roof became a golden roof, and the rickety walls turned into beautiful marble columns.

"Now, Baucis and Philemon, tell us your wishes," said the gods. "Ask what you will, it shall be granted."

Then Baucis and Philemon spoke quietly to each other. They did not have to consult long, for they knew what they wanted.

"Grant us that we may never be separated," they begged. "We have lived our lives together in love and peace. Do not let either of us have to bear the sorrow of being left without the other."

Their prayer was granted. Baucis and Philemon lived for many years as guardians of the temple. Then, one day when they were very, very old, they were changed into trees, both at the same moment. To this day, the people who live near that place point to a beautiful old oak tree and a lovely linden growing near a lake, and then they tell the story of Baucis and Philemon.

King Solomon and the Queen of Sheba

A TEST OF WISDOM

KING Solomon was the wisest man who ever lived. Not only did he know more than everybody in the whole world put together, but he also understood things that no one else could understand. It is said that he even understood the language of the birds and beasts, of insects and of flowers. He was King of Israel for many years, and people came to his court from all over the world in order to learn from him.

Far away from the land of Israel, there was a kingdom which was ruled by a queen who was very beautiful and learned, and she admired wisdom very much. Even in her distant kingdom, she had heard of the great wisdom of Solomon, and she made up her mind that she must go and see for herself if King Solomon was indeed as wise as everyone said. So she sent a message to the King, saying, "Most Gracious Majesty, the Queen of Sheba would be honored to visit you in your kingdom."

King Solomon loaded her messengers with magnificent gifts and sent them back to the queen with this message: "Great Queen, it is I who am honored. I await your visit with impatient joy."

So the Queen of Sheba set forth with many attendants. Finally she arrived in Jerusalem, the capital city of Israel. King Solomon greeted her with much pomp and ceremony. He arranged for a big feast to be held in her honor.

On the morning before the feast, the King was holding his court of justice, where people came to him with their quarrels, their problems, and their lawsuits. Suddenly there was a stir in the court. The King looked up in surprise as the court chamberlain announced, "Her Royal Highness, the Queen of Sheba!"

The queen curtsied low to the King. Then she beckoned to her servants, who brought forward a little table on which were placed two wreaths of flowers, both exactly alike.

"Great King," she said, "the whole world has heard of your wisdom. Indeed, even in my far-off kingdom, tales of your marvelous understanding have reached us. Finally I said to myself, 'Is it possible for a mortal man to be so wise? I must go and see for myself. If he is even half as wise as people say, it would be wonderful.'

"Now see, King, I have here on this table two garlands of flowers. So cunningly did my artist make them that to the eye and even to the touch, they seem exactly the same. But in truth, the flowers of one garland are real, but the flowers of the other garland are artificial. Can you tell which garland is real and which is false?"

"Can you tell which garland is real and which is false?"

A great silence fell over the court as the courtiers watched the scene; for the garlands were so marvelously wrought that no one in the court thought it possible to tell one from the other.

King Solomon gazed at the garlands for one long moment. Then he smiled and walked over to the window. "Open the window," he said to his servants. They did so, and the next moment the room was filled with a buzzing sound as a little bee flew into the room, from the garden outside. Straight as an arrow it flew. It did not hesitate for a moment. It settled on one of the garlands.

"That is the garland of real flowers," said King Solomon.

A sigh of admiration swept the room. The Queen of Sheba bowed low, as she said, "O great and wise King, they spoke truly. You are indeed the wisest of men. Happy would I be to sit at your feet and learn wisdom!"

The Princess
in the Tower

TRUE LOVE FINDS A WAY

KING Solomon was very rich. He had treasures of all kinds — gold and precious stones, magnificent palaces — everything a man could wish for. The king enjoyed all this wealth, but he had one treasure that he loved beyond anything in the world, and that was his sweet and lovely daughter. A rare young girl she was, too. For she cared not for the pleasures of the court, for dancing and worldly things. She was thoughtful and quiet, and she preferred walking alone in the garden to the excitement of gay company.

Suitors came from far and near to ask for the hand of the king's daughter. Many young men fell in love with her — handsome princes, gallant soldiers, noblemen of great wealth — but none of them could win her heart. One after the other, they came and tried to win the love of the beautiful princess, but, one after the other, they would be forced to give up and return to their own lands. As time went on, the princes began to despair of success and they gave up the quest.

Now, when the king saw this, he was greatly troubled for fear that his daughter would be left lonely and unwed, when he died. So he consulted the stars to see if he could discover what his daughter's fate would be. And what he found out vexed him deeply. For the stars told him that at a certain time, not far distant, his daughter would marry. She would not marry a prince or a king, however, but a poor young man of humble family.

"My daughter shall not marry beneath her, if I can prevent it," said the king to himself. "I will not have it so."

Then the king made a plan: He would hide his daughter away, where no suitor could reach her, until the time decreed by the stars had passed. In this way, he hoped to avert the fate he feared for his daughter.

So he found a lonely island, where ships never passed. On it was a castle with heavy gates and a wall round about it. The king had the castle furnished with costly silks and satins and handsome furniture. He had the kitchens filled with the finest foods. At the top of the tower he had prepared a beautiful apartment for the young princess, filled with her favorite books and musical instruments. Everything that could be thought of was provided for the young princess' comfort and amusement, except for one thing: no one was permitted to come to or go from the island. The king set seventy old men, Elders in Israel, in the castle to guard his daughter constantly, to see that no one approached the island. They were to watch the gates and to scan the seas on all sides, night and day, for this purpose. The king so ordered it.

Then, with his own hands, he locked and sealed every door in the castle and all the gates in the castle walls, and he sailed away.

Now just about this time, a poor young man set forth from his home to see the world. He was no ordinary young man, for he did not seek riches or power, but only wisdom. He wanted to wander through the world for a while, to learn about people in all countries and lands, in order to know their customs and ways. By this means, he hoped to gain understanding of his fellow men.

Wherever he went, people were kind to him, for he was a good and gentle youth, and handsome as well. But it happened that one dark and rainy night he found himself far from any houses, out in a bare and lonely spot. He looked all about for shelter, for it was raining hard, and he was tired and cold, but there was not a house to be seen — not even a tree beneath which he could huddle. Suddenly, he spied the carcass of an ox.

"How lucky I am!" he said to himself. "Even here, in the bare wilderness, I find shelter." And he lay down inside the skeleton of the ox.

Being tired, he soon fell into a deep sleep. While he was sleeping, a large eagle, seeing the carcass of the ox, swooped down, picked up the skeleton, with the young man inside, and flew off with it. Straight out toward the sea, the eagle flew, and it carried the young man inside the skeleton to the tower where the princess was hidden.

When the young man awoke, it was morning. He was astonished to find himself at the top of a high tower, surrounded by the sea on all sides. At that moment, the king's daughter stepped out, as was her custom, for her morning stroll along the castle wall. She was amazed to see a young man on her terrace.

"Who are you, and how did you get here?" she asked.

The young man, dazzled by her loveliness, could hardly collect his wits; nevertheless, he politely and clearly told her what had happened to him.

Soon the two young people were talking long and earnestly. And as they talked, they felt as if they had known each other all their lives. They fell in love.

The young man, hearing that she was the king's daughter, did not dare to ask her to marry him, although his heart yearned toward her. But the princess spoke honestly and unashamedly.

"If you love me, as you say, will you be my husband?" she said.

At these words, the youth cried out, "I swear to be your husband and to love you forever! See, I will seal my vow with my heart's blood!"

Then he let blood from his arm, and with it, he wrote the words he had just spoken. And the princess believed him and loved him with all her heart.

So she hid him in her bower, in her own apartment, where the Elders never came, for she feared for his life, if he should be discovered.

She was amazed to see a young man on her terrace.

In this way, the Elders knew nothing of what had happened, for the princess reported to them each day as usual. They were content.

When the date decreed by the stars had passed, King Solomon hurried to the island, for he had missed his daughter sorely. He examined each and every lock which he had placed on the many doors and gates, and he found that none of them had been broken. Then he ordered them to be opened, and he entered the castle.

"How fares my daughter?" he asked. "Is she well and safe?"

"She is well and safe," answered the Elders, and bowed low. "She is at this moment in her bower."

Then the king and all the Elders went to the maiden's rooms. When they opened the door, there stood a handsome youth, and the hand of the young princess was clasped in his.

"Who is this?" cried the king, and turned in wrath to the Elders.

But the Elders were dumbfounded, trembling with fear. They could not say a word, for a terror had seized them.

"Answer!" thundered the king. "Or I will have you beheaded on the spot!"

"Oh, lord king," they cried. "How can we answer you? What can we say? Day and night we watched. Not for one moment did we relax our guard. But if we must die for it, we cannot tell you how this youth came to be here."

Then the king turned to his daughter and, with flashing eyes, demanded, "Shameless girl, what is this young man doing here?"

Sweetly and tenderly, the maiden spoke: "Do not be angry, my father, for this thing has happened according to God's wish. God sent an eagle to bring my beloved to me. Neither locks, nor bars, nor high mountains, nor wide seas could have kept him from me. He is my husband in the sight of God. Take him and bless him, O my father."

Then the king bade the youth tell him how he had come. And the young man spoke fearlessly to the king and told everything that had happened. He spoke of his poverty, and of his mother and father whom he honored for their goodness and learning. He told of his wanderings and of the marvelous way in which he had been carried to the top of the castle in the middle of the sea. And then he spoke of the princess and of his great love for her. He showed the king the scroll which he had written with his blood, testifying to his eternal love.

And as the young man spoke, the king realized that this must be the poor youth about whom he had been warned. But his heart was filled with joy, for this was a goodly youth. And he said to himself, "Now I know that there is no wisdom, no cleverness, no power, that can withstand the will of the Lord."

And he blessed the youth and took him to his heart.

The Wise Bird and the Hunter

AN OLD HEBREW FABLE

A HUNTER once caught a bird in a trap. "Let me go," the bird pleaded. "It won't do you any good to kill me, for I'm not a large bird. If you roast me, all you'll get is a mouthful or two at the most. If on the other hand you lock me in a cage, I can promise you right now, I'll never sing a note for you. However, if you let me go, I will give you three pieces of wisdom which will bring you great happiness and success."

The hunter pondered over the bird's speech. "All right," he said. "Tell me your three pieces of wisdom and I will let you go."

"First," said the bird, "never believe a story that goes against your common sense. Secondly, don't regret what is done and cannot be undone." Then, cocking his head to one side, the bird concluded, "And the third piece of wisdom is, don't try to do the impossible."

"There's nothing so wise about that," scoffed the hunter. "I practice those teachings all the time. But since you are not much use to me anyway, I'll let you go."

No sooner was the bird released, than he flew to a high branch

. . . he lost his balance, fell out of the tree, and was badly hurt.

of a nearby tree. "Foolish man!" he said, "Did you think I was just an ordinary bird? Oh, no! Now I can tell you that I am much different from other birds. My heart is made of a precious ruby of great size and brilliance. If you had cut me open and taken out my heart, you might have been the richest man in the world."

Upon hearing this, the man cursed his folly in letting the bird go. He shook his fist at the bird in the tree. "I'll catch you, you rogue!" he cried in a rage of disappointment.

The hunter quickly started to climb the tree. But the bird flew to the tip of a high branch, well out of the man's reach. The hunter leaned far out, trying to lay his hands on the bird. But he lost his balance, fell out of the tree, and was badly hurt.

"So!" cried the bird. "You said there was nothing so wise about my words — that what I told you is only what you always practice! But the first thing I told you was never to believe anything that was contrary to common sense. Did anyone ever hear of a bird whose heart was made of a ruby? No. Yet you instantly believed my story."

"The next thing I said was don't regret what has been done and cannot be undone. You let me go — but then you instantly regretted it!"

"The last piece of wisdom was, don't waste your energies pursuing the impossible. How could you ever hope to catch me, a bird who can fly — just by your climbing a tree? Yet you persisted in your folly and tried to snare a winged bird with your bare hands."

The shaken hunter got to his feet, a bruised but wiser man.

Romulus and Remus

HOW ROME WAS FOUNDED

MANY, many years ago near what is now the city of Rome, there was a small city called Alba Longa. The king of Alba Longa was a gentle old man called Numitor. He was not a warrior. He wanted only to live in peace; to watch over his flocks and to be a loving father to his son and daughter.

But King Numitor had a younger brother, Amulius, who was cruel and warlike. Amulius wanted the kingdom for his own.

Amulius gathered about him a group of rough, wicked men. One day, when they knew that King Numitor was away at his farm in the country, Amulius and his evil henchmen surrounded the farm and attacked it. They killed the king's son and carried off the lovely young princess, Rhea Sylvia, and put her in prison. Then Amulius proclaimed himself king.

The people did not dare to fight against Amulius. They were unarmed. They could only stand by, helpless. The good and gentle King Numitor was exiled for life to his country farm. But now that his son was dead and his lovely young daughter was taken from him,

Numitor had little desire to live.

Several years went by. Though the people of Alba Longa hated and feared King Amulius, they were powerless to overthrow him. Then came news that filled all hearts with hope. Princess Rhea Sylvia had escaped from prison! She had been delivered by a mighty warrior; but who he was, no one knew.

When Amulius learnt the news, he was frightened and angry. He sent out men all over the land to search for the Princess.

But none could find a trace of Rhea Sylvia. A year passed, and still there was no sign of the princess. Then one day, two shepherds came to the palace and asked to see the king.

Standing before Amulius, they uncovered a large basket which they were carrying. In the basket were two tiny babes who seemed to be no more than a few weeks old.

"Yesterday, as you know, the river Tiber overflowed its banks," they told the king. "We were driving our sheep away from the river's edge, when suddenly we saw a woman standing on a rock amidst the swirling waters of the river. Not knowing who she was, we ran to help her! But when we drew near, we saw she was none other than the Princess Rhea Sylvia. We made a rush to seize her; but before we could reach her, she jumped into the river and was carried away by the rushing waters. She is surely drowned. But on the rock where she had stood, we discovered these twin babes. We are sure that it was Rhea Sylvia whom we saw, for here is the cloak that covered the babes. See, it is the Princess' own royal cloak."

When Amulius heard this, he cried, "Fools! Why did you not throw the babes into the river to die with their mother!"

"We did not dare to do so, except at your command," said the shepherds.

"Go now, then, and hurl them into the river!" shouted Amulius. "Get them out of my sight!"

So the two men carried the two infants back to the river. But they could not bring themselves to do the awful deed.

"How could I look at my own little ones, if I did so cruel a thing?" said one.

"I cannot bear to see them drown," said the other.

Just then they caught sight of a wooden trough, the kind that shepherds use to feed their sheep. "Let us place the children in the trough," said one, "and send it floating down the river. Then we will not have to see them drown."

The other shepherd agreed. They wrapped the little babies in their mother's cloak, placed them in the trough, and shoved it out into the stream. The wooden trough floated down the river just like a little boat.

"Poor helpless babes!" said the first shepherd. "If they do not die of drowning, they will die of starvation, or they will be devoured by some wild beast." And with heavy hearts, the two men made their way home.

All day, the little boat floated down the river. The current carried the boat against the shore, where it got stuck in a little cove.

Just then, a she-wolf who had lost her young in the flood, came down to the river's edge to drink. Her teats were heavy with milk, for the wolf had been nursing her young cubs. The sad-hearted animal mother was in a tame and gentle state. Hearing sounds, she trotted over to the little boat. Could these be her babies? What had happened to them, to change them so? Gently, the wolf pulled at the cloak which covered the infants. In just that way, she had carried her own little ones by the loose skin of their necks. The wolf lifted up the children in the cloak—both at one time, and carried them back to her den.

Many months later, when the floods had abated and the river was once more a narrow, quiet stream, a shepherd by the name of Faustulus came to the same spot. He was hunting for a wolf who had been devouring his master's sheep. Now he had finally tracked it down. The wolf's footprints led directly into a cave.

Faustulus closed in on the wolf. The animal turned round and gave fight. Faustulus lifted up his spear and, with one well-aimed blow, killed the beast on the spot. The shepherd thought he had best look into the wolf's den, to see if there were any cubs there. With spear in hand, he crept forward cautiously. At first, in the sudden darkness of the cave, he could see nothing. But when his eyes grew accustomed to the gloom of the den, he gasped with astonishment at what he saw. There, in a corner of the wolf's den sat two husky little babies!

They seemed to be about eight months old. Was it possible?

The wolf lifted up the children in the cloak . . .

Could he really be seeing two children, safe and sound in the den of a wild beast? Yet there they were; and from the appearance of a large cloak which Faustulus found next to the babies, and from the way they looked, dirty but happy, it seemed as if they had been there for a long time.

It was plain that the she-wolf which he had just killed, had cared for the babies just as she would have cared for her own young. She had turned on the shepherd in order to protect these little ones from him. Tenderly he wrapped the children in the cloak and brought them home to his wife.

"Oh, husband!" cried his wife, "do you not recognize this cloak? It is the cloak of our beloved Princess Rhea Sylvia. Do you not remember how last autumn when the floods raged over the countryside, people told how our dear Princess and her babes had been drowned? Let us keep them here with us, and tell no one about it. For if the cruel Amulius should hear of this, he would surely kill them. Shall we bestow less kindness on these helpless babes than did a wild beast?"

"You are right, good wife," answered Faustulus. "We shall do as you say. We may be poor in worldly goods, but we are rich, for we have twelve children of our own. We will bring up these little twin boys as our own. Amongst so many children, no one will notice two more."

So the twin boys were cared for by the poor shepherd and his wife. They were named Romulus and Remus. They were given the same food and the same loving care as their foster-sisters and brothers. But no one knew who they were, except old Faustulus and his wife.

Years passed. The twins, alike as two peas in a pod, grew to be young men. They were known as the sons of Faustulus. They were handsome, graceful and tall and soon gained a name for themselves as bold and fearless shepherds. They hunted wild beasts and fought with robbers. When Romulus and Remus were guarding the sheep, there were not many men nor beasts that dared molest the flocks of Faustulus.

Now just across the hillside where the sheep of Faustulus used to graze, lay the farm to which old Numitor had been banished. One day, Romulus sitting on the slope looked across the valley.

"Look how rich and green the grass is on old Numitor's hillside," said Romulus. "Let us drive our flocks over there to graze."

His companions agreed. So the bold young fellow led his sheep across to his neighbor's fields. Romulus knew that it was wrong, but he did it again and again because he loved to tease Numitor's shepherds. Numitor's men became angrier and angrier. They set a trap to catch Romulus. They caught one of his sheep and tied it to a post close to their own sheepfolds.

Sure enough, when Romulus noticed that one of his sheep was missing, he went back to search for it. Catching sight of the animal tied near Numitor's sheepfold, he ran forward to untie it. Then the shepherds of Numitor, who had been hiding behind a hedge, sprang forth and caught him.

"Ho!" they cried, "now we have you. Did you think you could trespass on our lands for long and go unpunished? Come along with us, bold fellow. We'll show you what happens to anyone who dares to steal grass that belongs to Numitor's sheep!" And with that they hustled him off to Numitor himself.

Now in those rough days, punishments were cruel and quick and what Romulus had done was considered a serious crime. When old Numitor saw the man who had been trespassing on his land, he said, "Take him away and kill him. Let people know how we deal with such robbers!"

Just then old Faustulus came rushing in. He had heard that Romulus had been caught by Numitor's men. Fearing the outcome, he had hastened to Numitor. Close behind him came Romulus' twin brother, Remus.

"Oh, Numitor," cried Faustulus, "you know not what you do! Would you kill your own grandson?"

"What!" cried Numitor, "you know well that I have no children. How then could I have grandchildren?"

Then Faustulus told him how Romulus and Remus had been mothered by a wolf. He told Numitor how he had found the infant boys in the wolf's den, and how he had cared for them.

"See this cloak. Is it not your daughter's own garment? Look at your grandsons. Does not their very countenances prove to you who they are!"

Numitor was convinced. With tears of joy in his old eyes, he stretched out his arms and gathered Romulus and Remus to his breast.

When Romulus and Remus discovered who they really were, they cried, "Down with false Amulius! Numitor is our king!"

The people of Alba Long now knew they had two strong young men to lead them. They rose up as one and attacked the palace. The wicked Amulius was killed and Numitor was restored to his kingdom.

Peace reigned once more, but Romulus and Remus were young and full of vigor. They were impatient with the slow and plodding ways of Alba Longa. So one day they came to their grandfather, King Numitor, and said, "Grandfather, this kingdom is too small for us. See, across the Tiber River there are wild and beautiful hills as yet unsettled by man. We would build us a city there and make a kingdom for ourselves."

So Romulus and Remus set forth across the Tiber with a band of bold and adventurous men. On the tallest of seven neighboring hills they started to build a city.

Alas! Before the work had gone far, Remus was accidentally killed. But the work continued under the guidance of Romulus. So today, on seven hills near the Tiber, stands the city of Rome named after its founder, Romulus. It is now one of the greatest and most beautiful cities in the world. And today, all over Italy, you will see statues of Romulus and Remus and the wolf who was their foster-mother.

The Story of Regulus

A ROMAN GENERAL KEEPS HIS WORD

ROME fought many wars, but none more bitter than against Carthage, Rome's mighty foe across the Mediterranean.

At one time, the fortunes of war turned against Rome, and Regulus, her great general, was taken prisoner. For many months he lay in prison, despairing of ever seeing Rome or his beloved wife and child again. Then one day his jailers threw open the door of his dungeon cell. They led Regulus into the presence of a great general of Carthage.

The Carthaginian general came quickly to the point. "Regulus," said he, "we will release you to go back to Rome if you will do one thing. Go before the Roman Senate, and tell them how the war is going — about the battles Rome has lost. Convince them that the time has come to make peace on our terms."

"And if the Senate will not agree to make peace on your terms?" Regulus asked.

"Then you must agree to return to prison," replied the enemy general. "We know you as a man of honor. Your word is good."

"I have returned as I promised."

"Very well," said Regulus. "I agree that if Rome will not make peace, I shall return to prison."

Regulus departed for Rome, and the Carthaginians congratulated themselves. Here was their chance to gain by cleverness what Carthage was no longer strong enough to win on the field of battle.

Regulus was received with rejoicing in Rome. The Senate was immediately assembled, and Regulus was called upon to address it. But he did not say what the Carthaginians thought he would.

"Fellow Romans!" said Regulus, "The Carthaginians are tired and weak. That is why they have released me to make peace. You must not listen to their words. If we attack quickly and with all the force at our command, we will surely conquer."

The Senate rose as one man and cheered. "You must lead the attack!" they cried. "Regulus will avenge his capture!"

Regulus shook his head sadly. "Nay, my countrymen," he said. "I have given my word that if Rome does not make peace, I shall return as a prisoner. That I must do."

With renewed heart, the Romans began their preparation for the attack that would defeat their ancient enemy. Regulus returned to Carthage and to certain death. When he was brought before the Carthaginian general, he said, "I have returned as I promised. The word of a Roman must be believed."

And indeed it was because of men like Regulus that the Romans were respected and admired throughout the ancient world.

Camillus and the Traitor

HOW A ROMAN DEALT WITH TREACHERY

CAMILLUS was a great Roman general who led his army against the powerful and warlike Etruscans. He had won victory after victory until at last the Roman legions were encamped in the plain below the important Etruscan city of Falerii. Situated atop a towering cliff, Falerii would be a difficult city to capture.

Camillus prepared to attack. While the preparations were going on, a man appeared in the Roman camp and demanded to see the general. He was led into Camillus' tent.

"Great Camillus," said the Etruscan. "I have come to do the Romans a great service. Know you that I am from the city of Falerii. I am the tutor of the sons of the leading men of the city. I have brought these boys through a secret mountain pass to yonder grove of trees. With these boys in your hands, you can easily force the city to surrender." He smiled slyly. "For this service," he continued, "you may reward me as you think I deserve."

Upon hearing this Camillus rose up in wrath. "You treacherous brute!" he cried. "We Romans do not make war with boys. When

"Let them drive the traitor back to his city!"

we win, we win by courage, labor and arms! Indeed I *shall* reward you as you deserve!"

Turning to his guards Camillus said; "Take him away! Tear off his clothes. Bind him with heavy bonds. Then give the young lads whips and rods. Let them drive the traitor back to his city!"

Needless to say, when the boys got back to their city and told of their tutor's treachery, the man was punished without pity. But when the Falerians heard of the noble action of Camillus, they decided they had best surrender. It would be no dishonor to surrender to so generous and honorable a foe.

Cincinnatus

THE MAN WHO WOULD NOT BE KING

"OH noble Roman Senators!" The spent runner was gasping for breath. " I bring you terrible tidings!"

"Our army —?" began a frightened Senator.

The runner nodded. "Our army. The Aequians have our army surrounded in a mountain pass not many leagues from Rome. Our men are fighting bravely, but there is no escape!"

Fear spread from the Senate chamber throughout Rome, just as ripples spread from a stone tossed in a pond. Soon the entire city was in a panic.

The usually grave Senate chamber was in an uproar.

"What can we do?" asked one white haired patriarch. "If our army is lost, Rome is lost. There are none left to defend our city but women and children and old men."

"You may be sure the Aequians will show us no mercy," said a second Senator. "Have they not boasted that they will sack Rome, kill all our men, and make slaves of our women and children? Where shall we turn? Who is there wise enough to lead us in our hour of peril?"

"Cincinnatus!" cried a third. "Cincinnatus is wiser than any of us."

The second Senator shook his head. "True, Cincinnatus is wise, but he is old. The kindest thing we can do is let him remain on the farm. What can he do? What can any of us do?"

But in despair the Senate seized upon the name of Cincinnatus. They sent a delegation to call on the old Roman at his farm outside the walls of Rome. They came upon him as he was ploughing his fields.

Cincinnatus looked up from his plough as the Senators approached. One glance told him that they were terribly disturbed and overwrought.

"Is all not well with Rome?" asked Cincinnatus anxiously.

"Alas, no!" replied one of the men. He went on quickly to tell Cincinnatus of Rome's peril. "You are known for your wisdom, Cincinnatus," he concluded. "In our ordeal the people of Rome are calling upon you to save us. The Senate has made you dictator of Rome to save our country from disaster."

Cincinnatus for all his years stood straight and proud. "I shall do what I can," he said. "I shall do what I must!"

Cincinnatus called for his wife to bring him his toga. Donning it, he left his plough, bade his wife farewell and started off with the Senators toward Rome.

When he arrived in the city, Cincinnatus found a scene of the

"I shall do what I can," he said. "I shall do what I must!"

wildest confusion and despair. Many were throwing their belongings together, preparing to flee the city. Others spoke of putting the city to the torch, to destroy Rome so as to leave nothing for the Aequians. Still others just walked aimlessly through the streets, wringing their hands and bemoaning their fate.

Cincinnatus calmed and rallied his people. "Citizens of Rome," he said. "If we are to die, far better it is that we die like Romans and not like sheep. But all is not yet lost. Our army is trapped but it is still fighting. We can still save ourselves. Who will follow Cincinnatus?"

The cries of "I, — I, — I will follow!" swelled to a roar. Old men girded on swords; young boys picked up spears. Behind Cincinnatus there marched out of Rome a rag-tag, makeshift, home guard army which would have caused most generals to sneer. But, though this was an army of old men and boys, it was an army of courage.

With scarcely a pause for rest or food, they marched until they reached the pass where the Roman legions were surrounded. Without a moment's hesitation, Cincinnatus ordered his men to attack. They threw themselves on the rear of the Aequian army, taking the enemy completely by surprise. Now the shoe was on the other foot! Now the Aequians were themselves trapped between the Roman army they had thought defeated, and the new army which Cincinnatus had hastily thrown together. Defeat for Rome turned into victory. The Aequians were destroyed and Rome was saved!

How great was the rejoicing throughout Rome! As he marched back victorious, through the city gates, the grateful people hailed Cincinnatus as their deliverer. "Be our king!" they cried. "All power to Cincinnatus!"

The Senate, heedful of the popular clamor, also voted to make Cincinnatus king. But Cincinnatus refused. "Rome is safe," he said. "That is all I wanted. We need no kings in Rome."

So Cincinnatus went back to the plough. He had ruled Rome for just sixteen days. He did not seek to be his country's dictator. It was enough for him that he had been its deliverer.

Cornelia's Jewels

A MOTHER'S LOVE AND PRIDE

IN the ancient days of Rome, there lived a widow named Cornelia. She was of noble birth and had once been very wealthy. But since her husband's death, she had become quite poor. With her two young sons, she still lived in the handsome mansion her husband had given her. But no longer were there servants about to wait on Cornelia. In her slim purse, there was little money for luxuries.

One day, one of her wealthy friends came to visit her. The two ladies sat in the garden and talked of many things.

"How noble and beautiful Cornelia looks," thought her friend. "One would never guess that she is so poor. Poor thing, it must be hard to have so little now, when once she had so much."

The lady who thought these thoughts was elegantly dressed. Her arms were covered with golden bracelets. Magnificent pearls hung around her neck. Cornelia, on the other hand, wore no jewels at all. Her lovely neck and arms were bare.

Cornelia's friend looked at her, and in a burst of pity exclaimed, "Dear Cornelia, is it true, as I have heard it whispered—is it true

"I am very rich, for these are my jewels."

that you are now poor—that you have no jewels?"

Cornelia rose and smiled. She drew her two young sons to her side and standing proud and straight she answered, "No, it is not true. I am very rich, for these are my jewels."

Years later, these two sons grew up to become leaders of their country. They never forgot their mother's great love. They never forgot their mother's great pride in them. And even today, many hundreds of years later, people love to think back on Cornelia's words and to remember that he whose wealth is counted only in gold and jewels is poor indeed.

The Tale of the Clever Deer

HOW BRAINS OVERCAME BRAWN

A LITTLE deer was quietly nibbling some grass, when suddenly a tiger jumped out of the bushes. At the sight of the fierce tiger, the little deer's·heart stood still with fear. But since there was no way to escape, he bravely stood his ground.

Now ordinarily, the tiger would have eaten up so small and tender an animal, but this tiger had never seen a deer before.

"What are those things growing out of your head?" asked the tiger.

"Those are horns," said the little deer.

"Of what use are horns?" asked the tiger.

"Why, they are used especially to fork tigers with," said the clever little deer.

"Really?" replied the tiger. "And what are all those white spots on your body for?"

"Don't you know?" said the little deer. "I thought everybody knew that. Every time I eat a tiger, a spot appears on my body. As you can see, I've eaten so many tigers that I'm practically covered with spots."

When the tiger heard this, he was so scared that he bounded away into the forest.

Pretty soon he met a fox. He told the fox of the fearsome animal he had just met—the animal who forked tigers with his horns and who had eaten so many tigers.

"You can't be talking about the little deer," laughed the fox. "Oh, what a trick he has played on you!"

The tiger couldn't believe that the little deer had fooled him so completely. But the fox said, "If you don't believe me, I'll show you myself. Just let me ride on your back and lead me to the deer. You'll soon see."

So they set out. When the little deer saw the tiger returning with the fox on his back, he knew at once that the fox had told the tiger the truth. He had to think fast to save himself, and think fast he did.

"Ho, there, friend fox!" he called. "I see you have kept your promise. You told me that you would bring a fine tiger for me to devour, and that surely is a beauty you're bringing me now!"

When the tiger heard this, he needed no more convincing. He darted back into the forest—with the fox in his mouth! And the clever little deer was saved!

The Weighing of the Elephant

A BOY SHOWS THE WAY

ONCE, the great General Ts'ao Ts'ao was presented with a huge elephant. In those days, an elephant was a rare sight in that part of the world, and the Chinese general was filled with wonder and excitement.

"What a marvelous, enormous beast!" he cried. "I wonder how much he weighs? Someone please weigh the animal for me."

But no one could do so, for they did not have a scale big enough.

"We are sorry, sir, but we cannot weigh the elephant. As you can see, we do not have a scale which is large enough," said his captains and his aides. "No one can weigh an elephant."

Just then, up spoke General Ts'ao Ts'ao's little son.

"Oh, Father," he said, "I can weigh the elephant for you."

"What?" cried his father. "You think you can do what all my officers cannot do? How do you expect to do it?"

"It is simple," said the boy. "Just lead the elephant onto one of

"Just lead the elephant onto one of your big boats."

your big boats. The weight of the elephant will cause the boat to sink somewhat. The water will make a line around the boat. Then take the elephant ashore. Now fill the boat with stones until it sinks to the level of the watermark. Then, if you weigh each of the stones, and add up the amounts, you will know how much the elephant weighs."

"Ah, yes," said the General, "it is simple, now that you tell us, but only a genius could have figured it out the first time. I am proud of you, my son."

The General and
the Arrows

ONCE it happened that an army, headed by two generals, had to fight a battle. But they were in a bad condition, for they had almost no arrows left. It would take them many days to make enough arrows for all their men, but it was important that they attack their enemy within the next day or two, while they had the enemy cornered.

"What can we do?" said Chon-Yu, the first general. "It's no use. This was our big chance, and we have lost it for lack of arrows."

"Don't give up so easily," said the other general, whose name was Liang. "There must be something we can do."

"Oh, no," cried Chon-Yu, "there's nothing to be done."

"Well, then, if that's how you feel, will you agree to leave everything to me?" said Liang. "I have an idea that we will get the arrows, and we will win this battle. But you must do just as I say."

The first general agreed. Then Liang ordered twenty ships to

And the arrows stuck in the straw dummies!

be readied for sailing. On each ship he had placed a crew, not of sailors, but of straw dummies dressed to look like warriors. On each ship he also placed a few real soldiers, equipped with drums and trumpets.

Then, as night was beginning to fall, he set sail with the ships until he came within shooting distance of the enemy camp. By then, it was dark. Now Liang ordered his men to beat their drums and blow their trumpets.

The enemy, hearing the tremendous noise, thought that a big army was attacking them. Quickly, they ran to their battle stations and sent volleys of arrows in the direction from which the noise came. Because it was dark, they could not see clearly, and they thought that the ships were loaded with many soldiers. Volley after volley of arrows were loosed against their unseen foe. And the arrows stuck in the straw dummies!

When General Liang saw that he had thousands of arrows, he ordered his ships to return to camp. There he gave General Chon-Yu more than enough arrows for the whole army—a gift from the enemy itself!

The Milkmaid and Her Pail

A FABLE BY AESOP

A MILKMAID was on her way to market with a pail of milk on her head.

As she walked along she said to herself, "With the money I get from this milk, I will buy some setting eggs. From the eggs, I will get some chicks. I will raise the chicks until they are big enough to sell. With the money I get from the chickens, I will buy a beautiful gown. When I wear the gown, I will look so beautiful that all the men will pay court to me. But I will act so proud; I will shrug my shoulders, so!"

As she shrugged, she tossed her head. The pail of milk tumbled down and the milk spilled over the ground.

Don't count your chickens before they are hatched.

The Boy Who Cried Wolf

A FABLE BY AESOP

THERE was once a shepherd boy who used to mind his sheep far out of town on a lonely hillside. The days wore heavy on his hands and one day the lad thought of a way to drum up some excitement. He ran down the hill shouting, "A wolf! A wolf!"

At this, the neighboring farmers, thinking that a wolf was devouring the boy's flock, dropped their work and ran to his aid. However, when they got to the hillside, the boy laughed and said, "I was just playing a joke." The men were quite annoyed and went back to their work.

Some few days later the boy tried the same thing again. Again the farmers dropped their tools and ran to his assistance. When they saw that the boy had fooled them a second time, they were very angry.

The very next day, however, a wolf did appear.

"Wolf! Wolf!" cried the boy. But this time the farmers did not believe him. They refused to help him and many of the boy's sheep were eaten.

A liar is not believed even when he tells the truth.

The Fox and the Crane

A FABLE BY AESOP

A FOX once invited a crane to dinner. The fox served the soup in a very shallow dish. He thought it was very funny that the crane, with his long beak, was not able to drink any of the soup. Chuckling to himself at his joke, the fox lapped up all the soup.

Then he said, "My dear crane, I am sorry to see that you are not eating anything. Was the soup not to your liking?"

"Oh, everything is just fine," answered the crane. "And now you must do me the honor of paying *me* a visit."

When the fox came to the crane's house and sat down to dinner, a very tall jar was placed in front of him. It was so tall and narrow that the fox could not get his snout into it.

"I am so glad to be able to return your courtesy," said the crane as he reached his long beak into the jar. "I hope you enjoy your dinner every bit as much as I did mine when I visited you."

A person gets what he deserves.

The Bundle of Sticks

A FABLE BY AESOP

AN old man once called his sons to him. "I shall soon die," he said, "but before I leave you, I want to show you something of great importance. But first go and gather some thin sticks for me."

His sons did as they were bid.

Then the father gave each of them a stick and said, "Please break this for me." Each of them broke his stick with great ease.

Then the father took all the remaining sticks and placed them together. "Now," he said to one of his sons, "break all these sticks at one time." The son tried and tried but could not do so. Nor could any of the other boys break the bundle of sticks.

"I am sure," said their father, "that you know what I mean to tell you by this. Each one of you, alone, is weak; but if you stay together, you will be strong."

In unity there is strength.

The Fox and the Crow

A FABLE BY AESOP

A WILY old fox once saw a crow fly from a kitchen window to the branch of a tree. In her beak, the crow held a nice big piece of cheese.

"That's for me," said the fox to himself. So he went to the foot of the tree and said, "Good morning, Mistress Crow! How well you are looking today. You are quite the loveliest of all birds. I am sure that you sing sweeter than any other bird in the world! How I would love to hear a song from you."

These words so tickled the crow's vanity that she could not resist his request. She lifted up her head, opened her mouth wide, and began to caw at the top of her lungs. No sooner had she done this when the piece of cheese fell to the ground. Quick as a flash, the clever fox gobbled it up.

"Thank you," said the fox. "That is all I wanted."

Do not trust flatterers.

The Boy and the Nuts

A FABLE BY AESOP

A BOY once came upon a jar filled with nuts. He reached his hand into the jar and grabbed a handful of nuts. But when he tried to pull his hand out, it could not pass through the narrow neck of the jar.

When he saw this he began to cry, for he hated to let go of any of the nuts.

His father said to him: "Greedy lad! If you take half as much, you will have something. This way you get nothing!"

Don't grab more than you can use!

The Man and the Boy and the Donkey

A FABLE BY AESOP

A MAN and his son with their donkey were once walking along the road to market. As they walked along they met a couple.

"Did you ever see anything so silly?" said the man to his wife. "Two men walking when they have a donkey with them. What is a donkey for but to carry a man?"

Hearing this, the man put his son on the back of the donkey and they went on their way. Soon they met two countrymen. "Did you ever see such a terrible thing?" one of them cried. "The strong young man rides while his poor old father must walk." So the boy dismounted from the donkey and the father got on instead.

They hadn't gone very far when they met two women. "Look at that heartless father!" exclaimed one of them. "His poor little son must walk while he rides." At that the man said to his son, "Come up here with me. We will both ride on the donkey."

They both rode for a short while till they reached a group of men. "Aren't you ashamed!" they called out, "overloading a poor little donkey like that." So the man and his son both climbed off

The donkey fell off the bridge into the water.

the donkey.

They thought and thought. Finally they got hold of a tree and cut it into a long pole. Then they tied the donkey's feet to it. They then raised the pole to their shoulders and went on their way carrying the donkey.

As they crossed a bridge, the donkey who did not like being tied up kicked one of his feet loose, causing the father and son to stumble. The donkey fell off the bridge into the water. Because its feet were tied, it drowned!

If you try to please everyone, you will please no one.

The Crow and the Pitcher

A FABLE BY AESOP

ONE hot summer's day a crow, half-dead of thirst, found a pitcher with a little water at the bottom. But the pitcher was so tall he could not reach down far enough to get at the water. If he did not have some water, he would surely die. So the crow thought and thought.

Then he picked up a stone with his beak and dropped it into the pitcher. He kept dropping stones into the pitcher until the water rose high enough for him to reach with his beak. Then he drank it.

Necessity is the mother of invention.

The Lion and the Mouse

A FABLE BY AESOP

ONCE upon a time a little mouse was caught by a large lion. As the lion opened his jaws to devour him, the little mouse cried, "Oh, great king of beasts, please let me go. I am so small, not even a mouthful for you. And who knows? Some day I might be able to help you."

"Help *me*?" said the lion. "How could a little thing like you ever help me. However, I will let you go this time."

Soon afterwards the lion was caught in a net which had been set to trap him. He roared in anger and fear. The little mouse heard him and ran to his aid. "Oh, king," he said, "you were kind to me. Now the time has come when I can help you." Then the mouse gnawed at the ropes of the net. In a little while, the lion was set free.

No one is so poor or weak that he cannot return a kindness.

Then the mouse gnawed at the ropes of the net.

The Wolf and the Crane

A FABLE BY AESOP

A WOLF once got a bone stuck in his throat. In great pain he ran to the crane for help. "I will help you," answered the crane, "if you give me a reward."

"Of course," answered the wolf, "anything you want. Only quickly put your long beak down my throat and pull out this bone."

The crane did so. Then he asked for his reward.

"Get off with you!" answered the wolf. "You can consider yourself lucky that you were able to put your head into a wolf's mouth and not be eaten."

He who helps only for the sake of reward deserves nothing.

" . . . put your long beak down my throat and pull out this bone."

The Fox and the Grapes

A FABLE BY AESOP

A FOX was walking along the road, when he spied some luscious looking grapes growing on a high trellis. "My, they look good!" he said. He jumped up but he could not reach them. He tried again and again but to no avail. Finally he looked angrily at the grapes and said, "Hmmm, who wants the old grapes? They're very likely sour anyway."

It is easy to despise what you cannot have.

The City Mouse and the Country Mouse

A FABLE BY AESOP

ONCE upon a time, a city mouse invited his country cousin to visit him. "Now you will see how wonderful life in the city is," he said. "Why, we have the best of everything."

The city mouse led the country mouse into the dining room. The table was strewn with all kinds of delicious morsels. No sooner had they started to eat when they heard a terrible barking and growling.

The country mouse was frozen with terror. "What is that?" he cried.

"Why that is only the dog of the house," said the city mouse.

"Only!" cried the country mouse. "This is no place for me!"

The next moment the door flew open and an enormous dog ran into the room. The mice just managed to escape in time.

"Goodbye, my dear cousin, goodbye!" said the country mouse.

"What!" exclaimed the city mouse. "Are you going so soon?"

"Indeed I am!" said the country mouse. "This is no life for me."

Better a crust of bread in peace than the finest of luxuries in fear.

The Foolish Dog and his Reflection

A FABLE BY AESOP

THERE was once a dog who was given a fine, meaty bone. With the bone firmly between his teeth the dog trotted homeward, thinking of what a fine meal he was going to enjoy.

On the way he had to cross a narrow bridge over a brook. As he looked over the side of the bridge, he caught sight of his own reflection in the water. Thinking that what he saw was another dog carrying a bone between his teeth, the foolish animal made up his mind that he would have that bone, too.

He leaned over and snapped at the dog beneath him. As he did so, the bone he carried fell out of his mouth into the water and was lost.

Be careful that you don't lose what you have by seeking more!

The Wind and the Sun

A FABLE BY AESOP

THE wind and the sun were having an argument. Each claimed to be stronger than the other. While arguing, they saw a man coming down the road and the sun said, "All right, this is our chance to settle the matter. Whoever can make that man take off his coat is the stronger. You begin."

The sun hid behind a cloud and the wind went to work. It blew and it blew, but the harder it blew the tighter the man held his coat around him. Finally, the wind had to give up.

Then the sun came out. It shone in all its glory upon the man. Soon the man opened his coat and smiled. The sun beat down upon him stronger and stronger. Finally the man was so warm that he took off his coat.

Kindness works better than harshness.

The Wolf and the Kid

A FABLE BY AESOP

A WOLF was once walking along the road when a kid, who was standing on a roof top, caught sight of him. "Ho there, you wretched beast!" called the little kid. "Be off with you, you vagabond! What are you doing here where decent people live?"

The wolf looked up at the kid and said, "You talk mighty bold, for you know that I cannot reach you."

It is easy to be brave from a distance.

Thor and the Giants

A FAMOUS TRIAL OF STRENGTH

JUST as the ancient Greeks told of their gods and the marvelous things they did, so too did the ancient Norsemen relate wonderful stories about the gods they imagined. According to these stories, the Norse gods dwelt in Asgard, high up in the sky, where they were ruled over by Odin, their king. Ordinary mortals dwelt in Midgard; and there was a race of giants, the enemies of both gods and men, who lived in a region called Jotunheim whose chief city was called Utgard.

Now the Norse gods dearly loved adventure. One day, three of the gods decided to seek danger and excitement by journeying to Jotunheim, the land of the giants.

One of the adventurous three was Thor the Thunderer, Odin's youngest son. He was the strongest of all the gods and possessed a wonderful hammer which destroyed whatever it was hurled against. When Thor hurled his hammer, thunder resounded in the skies.

The second of the three gods was Thor's half-brother, Loki the Red, so called because of the flaming color of his beard. His mother was a giantess, and so Loki was really a half-giant. As such, he was often mischievous and evil. So shrewd and clever was he however, that when he was on his good behavior many of the other gods sought him out as a companion.

The third of the three gods to make the journey was Thialfi the Runner, who could run more swiftly than anything on the earth or in heaven.

It was the custom of the gods to travel in disguise when they journeyed from Asgard. So, in their many days of travel, none who saw the three adventurers knew who they were.

As they drew near Jotunheim, the three travelers met an enormous giant, who greeted them in friendly fashion and led them along the road to Utgard.

Soon the city came into view. It was an awesome sight. So high were the walls of Utgard that Thor and his companions could scarcely see the top. They were welcomed with great hospitality by the king. But despite their disguises, Utgard's ruler knew immediately who they were.

"If I do not mistake me," he said with a smile of scorn, "that striping yonder must be the god Thor. Mayhap he is of greater strength than he looks, but to me he looks like a puny fellow. Tell me, Thor, in what feats of skill and strength do you and your companions deem yourselves champions?"

The gods from Asgard did not like the giant's tone of mockery, for they were accustomed to great respect.

He drank with mighty gulps . . .

"The feat that I know," Loki replied angrily, "is to eat quicker than anyone else; and in this, I am ready to give proof against anyone who may choose to compete with me."

"That will indeed be a feat," said the giant king. "And you shall be tried forthwith."

He ordered one of his men, a giant named Logi, to come forward. Logi and Loki each took a place at opposite ends of a long trough filled with enormous chunks of meat. When the signal was given, Logi began to eat from his end and Loki began to eat from the other end until they met in the middle of the trough. So quickly did the two contestants eat that in a matter of moments, the food was all gone. But Loki the god, had eaten only the meat, while Logi the giant, had eaten the bones and the trough as well! So all the company judged that Loki had lost.

The king of the giants then asked what feat young Thialfi could perform. Thialfi, who was known as the swiftest runner in the world, said he would run a race with anyone who was matched against him.

"That is indeed something to boast of," said the king. "In Midgard or in Asgard, you may well be the swiftest runner; but you are now in Utgard where dwell the giants. We shall soon see whether your boast is as vain as I judge it to be."

He arose and led the whole company to a large meadow many miles long, especially laid out for racing. He then called a young giant named Hugi and bade him race against Thialfi.

The signal for the start was given. Thor and Loki watched with bated breath. But although Thialfi flew along as fleet as the wind, he was outdistanced by Hugi who won the race, without even getting out of breath.

The king then spoke scornfully to Thor. "Now, Thor — *mighty* Thor, as you are called in other places — let us hope that you will do better than your companions. I would not like to be disappointed in all of you. Tell me what you would do?"

Thor, burning with shame at the defeat of his party, answered angrily that he would try a drinking match with anyone. The king then ordered his cup-bearers to bring in a large drinking horn.

"Good drinkers amongst us can empty this horn at a single draught," he said. "Most of us empty it in two; but even the puniest one amongst us can do it in three. Let us see if you can do it in three draughts."

Thor looked at the horn. It did not seem to be of an extraordinary size, and Thor felt sure that he could empty it easily. He set it to his lips and without drawing breath, pulled long and deeply. But when he set the horn down and looked in it he could scarcely believe his eyes. It seemed as if he had drunk nothing! Thor took a deep breath, and started his second draught. He drank with mighty gulps, until he thought his heart would burst. But when he put down the horn, it seemed that he had drunk off only a little from the top.

Then Thor was filled with wrath. "This time," he thought, "I will surely drain the cup." He drank and drank until it seemed that there could be nothing left in the horn. Then he set down the horn with an enormous sigh and looked. The liquid had gone down less than half the depth of the horn. Thor had failed!

"I see now plainly," said the king, "that you are even more puny than I thought. But maybe you would try another test?"

"What new trial do you propose?" asked Thor.

"We have a very trifling game here," answered the king. "Our children play it. It consists merely of lifting my cat from the ground."

As the king spoke, a large grey cat sprang out in front of them. Thor immediately stepped forward. Placing his hand under the cat's belly, he tried to lift it from the ground. But the cat, lengthening and lengthening itself, arched its back like a span of a bridge. Thor tugged and tugged but he could not manage to lift more than one of the cat's four feet off the floor.

"O ho!" laughed the king. "My poor little Thor! Even my cat is too strong for you to lift."

At this, Thor grew terribly angry. "Let me wrestle against a person, not a cat, and I will show you!" The king of Utgard looked at his men who sat around enjoying themselves hugely.

"I see not one of my warriors here who would not think it was beneath him to wrestle with you," said the king. "However, here is an old woman, my nurse Elli. Let us see how you stand up to her."

"No," answered Thor, "I will not wrestle with a woman."

"Mayhap you are afraid?" taunted the king.

At this, Thor sprang forward, ready for the struggle. Thor

grasped the old crone tightly in his iron arms, but she seemed not to mind it at all. The harder Thor pressed her, the stronger she seemed. It was as if she were made of iron. Finally, after a long and violent struggle, Thor began to lose his footing. With a quick turn, the old woman pulled him down upon one knee. She was the winner! In shame and anger, Thor withdrew. His heart was sore, for the giants had shamed the three gods in every test.

Early the next morning, Thor and his companions made ready to leave. The king of the giants accompanied them to the walls of the city. "Tell me truly now, brother Thor," said the giant king, "do you now think you are as mighty a fellow as you thought before you entered our gates? Or do you finally see that there are folk who are even stronger than you?"

Thor was still angry and ashamed but he had to speak the truth. "My name will be a joke amongst your people," he said. "They will call me Thor the Weakling. I must confess that you have beaten us soundly."

The king was pleased with the humble and honest way in which Thor spoke. "Nay," he answered, "hang not your head in shame. In truth, you have not done so ill as you think. Now I will tell you. By magic alone you were beaten."

"When you came to my city, I was greatly frightened for I knew then as I know now, your great strength. In every contest, you and your fellows were outwitted only by dint of our magic, not by our strength. Loki ate marvelously but Logi who ate with him was none other than Fire; and nothing in the world can devour as rapidly as fire. Thialfi here is a runner as swift as the wind, but Hugi who ran against him is Thought, and who can keep pace with the speed of thought? You, Thor, strove bravely; and truth to tell, I am indeed envious of your great strength and skill. When you drank from the horn (thinking you had done so poorly), in truth you had performed a miracle. You knew it not, but the end of the horn was set out in the ocean. Your mighty draughts have drained countless rivers dry; and the ocean itself is sunk low in its banks. The cat which you almost lifted — it was no cat, but the great serpent Midgard, whose body encircles the whole world. You raised it so high that he almost touched Heaven. How terrified we giants were when we saw you lift one of his mighty feet off the ground! And as for your wrestling match with old Elli — why, Elli is none other than Age itself. There is no one who ever lived who can overcome age. So grieve not, mighty Thor, for you were beaten by tricks. Now we must part. It is best that we should never meet again. And truly I tell you that never again shall I dare to let you step into my city. If such a thing should happen, I should overcome you again by magic if that were possible, for I doubt that I could do it any other way."

Then Thor and his companions returned to Asgard, as sure of their strength as they once were, but more humble.

The Apples of Youth

HOW ASGARD'S TREASURE WAS SAVED

HIGH in the heavens, in a cloud kingdom called Asgard, the Norse gods dwelt under the watchful eye of Odin their king. But the gods, who loved travel and adventure, did not always stay in Asgard. From time to time they liked to disguise themselves and wander on the earth, where men lived, and below the earth, where dwelt their enemies the giants.

On day Odin, weary of governing Asgard, decided to seek release in such a journey. He called upon his brother Hoenir and his half-brother Loki to be his traveling companions. Now Hoenir was a true god, noble and brave and good. Loki, however was by birth a half giant. As such he was not always to be trusted. Still, Loki could be a gay companion, which was why Odin chose him to go along.

In a merry mood the three gods crossed the rainbow bridge which led down from Asgard to the rest of the world. All that day they traveled over mountains and plains, over great rivers and waste places. Toward nightfall they were ravenously hungry. So they searched until they caught sight of a herd of oxen feeding in a grassy field. "There!" shouted Loki. "There is our supper!" In a matter of moments an ox was slain and roasting over a crackling fire.

The hungry gods could hardly wait for the meat to be cooked. Finally they judged that it was done, and lifted it from the fire. But strange to say, when they cut into it they found the meat as raw as when it first went on the spit. Loki shrugged and hung up the meat again. The gods heaped more wood on the fire until they had a towering blaze. This time they allowed the meat to roast even longer than at first. But again, when they began to carve it they found that it was still raw!

"Can it be that the meat is bewitched," asked Hoenir in amazement. Just then they heard a strange sound that seemed to come from a nearby oak tree. Peering up at the top of the tree, they spied an enormous eagle.

"Ho! Ho!" cried the eagle. "The meat *is* bewitched, and it is I who have bewitched it! Give me my share and you will find that the meat will cook as fast as you please."

"Come down and take your share," cried the hungry gods.

The eagle flew down, but instead of taking just a share, he grasped the whole ox in his talons and started to fly away!

"You thief!" roared Loki. "Drop that ox this instant!" Loki seized a long pole and struck at the eagle with all his might.

Then a strange thing happened. The pole stuck to the eagle and Loki was lifted high into the air. The bewildered Loki clung to the pole with all his strength. If he let go he would be dashed to pieces on the ground! The bird flew toward a far mountain.

"Loki," said the eagle, "no one can help you now except me. But if you will promise to do what I ask, you shall go free."

"Anything!" cried Loki. "Anything you say! Only let me go."

"Though I am disguised as an eagle I am really Thiasse, the giant," continued the bird. "You ought to love me, Loki, for you yourself are partly a giant."

"Oh, yes," moaned the thoroughly miserable Loki. "I dearly love you, but tell me, only tell me what you want of me!"

By this time they had reached the mountain, and Thiasse set Loki down. But he did not release him from the grasp of his strong claws. "I am growing old," said Thiasse. "There is but one thing that can make me young again. I must have the magic apples of youth that Idun keeps in her golden casket. You, Loki, must get them for me."

Loki grew pale as he heard this. "Oh giant!" he cried. "Idun's apples are the most precious treasure in all Asgard. Without them the gods themselves would grow old and die. I could never steal them from Idun. Not only does she guard them better than life itself, but if she should cry out, everyone in all Asgard would rush to her rescue."

"How difficult your task is does not interest me," said Thiasse. "I must have the apples and you have promised to do anything I ask. Clever as you are, you will be able to find a way."

Loki thought and thought. He hit upon a terrible but cunning plan. "I will do it, Thiasse," he said. "In one week I will bring you not only the apples, but the fair Idun herself. But you must not forget the terrible risk I shall take. In return, you must allow me to keep young by eating of the apples."

"Agreed," said the eagle. He picked up Loki again and flew swiftly back the way he had come. Then, swooping down he dropped Loki on a soft bed of moss close by Odin and Hoenir. The other two were glad and surprised to see Loki again; they feared he might have been devoured by the eagle. The three gods decided they had had enough of adventuring, and returned to Asgard.

Loki watched for his chance to carry out his wicked plan. A few mornings later he strode to the meadow where the lovely Idun sat amongst the flowers. The golden casket containing the apples was on her knees. Idun greeted Loki pleasantly. "Good morning, Loki," she said. "Have you come for a bite of the magic apples?"

"Whatever for?" answered Loki. "I do not need your apples any longer. This very morning I have found some apples which are sweeter by far, and more magical than yours."

Idun frowned. "That cannot be, Loki," she said. "There are no apples as wonderful as mine. Where have you found these apples of which you speak?"

"Oho, not so fast!" said Loki. "I will not tell anyone the place. I will say, however that it is in a little wood not very far from here. But no one could ever find it without me."

. . . the eagle fastened his claws in her clothing and flew away . . .

Idun was more curious and more anxious than ever. She began to plead and coax. At last Loki said, "Well, all right, then, Idun, I will show you the place. But remember, it must be a secret between you and me."

"Oh, yes," agreed Idun eagerly. "Come, let us go now while no one is looking."

Loki led Idun off. They walked and walked. Suddenly Idun noticed with alarm that they were outside of Asgard. "Oh, Loki," she said, "I mustn't leave Asgard."

"Don't worry," said Loki. "It is not very far." So on they went.

Without a moment's warning, there came a rustling of great wings. Down swooped Thiasse in the shape of an eagle. Before Idun could even scream, the eagle fastened his claws in her clothing and flew away toward the land of the giants. Loki waited till nightfall to slink back into Asgard, hoping that no one had seen him.

The next morning when the gods looked for Idun she was nowhere to be found! They were terribly frightened. If Idun and her apples were not quickly found, all the gods of Asgard would grow old and die. A great council was called.

Finally one of the gods remembered that the previous morning he had seen Idun walking with Loki. Since she had not been seen afterwards, it became clear that Loki must have had a part in her disappearance. The wrath of the gods was terrible. They seized Loki and threatened to kill him instantly unless he told them what he had done with Idun.

The terrified Loki confessed the truth. Odin said, "If you do not bring back Idun from the land of the giants, you will never escape punishment, and will surely die a horrible death."

Loki trembled. "How can I bring her back?" he asked?

"That is for you to discover," was Odin's only reply.

Loki thought for a moment. Then he said, "If the goddess Freia will lend me her falcon dress, I will bring Idun back. The giant Thiasse dresses as an eagle; therefore I must disguise myself as a bird before I can outwit him." Freia agreed.

When Loki donned the falcon's guise he looked exactly like a great brown hawk. He flapped his wings and off he went. Over mountains and forests Loki flew until finally he arrived at the palace of Thiasse. Luckily for Loki, Thiasse had gone fishing in the sea and Idun sat weeping and alone, imprisoned in the palace.

Hearing a light tap on her window, Idun looked up and saw a great brown bird on the ledge. She jumped up in fright, but the bird nodded pleasantly and said, "Don't be afraid, Idun. I have come to set you free. I am Loki, your friend."

"Loki!" she cried. "You are no friend of mine."

"You must believe me," said Loki. "I have come to take you back to Asgard. We must hurry before Thiasse returns."

"But how can I get out?" Idun asked. "My door is locked, and this window is barred."

"I will change you into a nut. Then I can lift you through the bars." Idun agreed, and Loki who was a skilled magician quickly turned her into a nut. Grasping the nut in one of his falcon's claws, and the casket in the other, Loki flew off towards Asgard.

In a little while, Thiasse came home. Finding Idun and the magic apples gone, he instantly guessed what had happened. Quickly he put on his eagle dress and set out in pursuit of the falcon.

Now an eagle is bigger and stronger than any other bird, and even though Loki had a good head start, the eagle rapidly shortened the distance between them. Loki was terrified; he was sure the swift flying eagle would overtake him. Finally Asgard loomed ahead. But the eagle was close, dangerously close behind Loki. The gods, who were gathered all along the rainbow bridge, watched breathlessly as the eagle gained swiftly on the falcon. Then Odin knew he must do something to save the falcon with its precious burden. He gave rapid orders. Soon all the gods were at work gathering wood and chips and piling them on the walls of Asgard. As soon as Loki had managed to fly over the wall the gods put torches to the pile of wood. In a moment a wall of flame soared into the sky. Thiasse the eagle, flying too fast to stop, flew straight into the roaring flames and perished.

There was great rejoicing in Asgard. Idun, changed back once again into a fair lady, gave each of the gods a morsel of the apples of youth. They grew young and beautiful and strong, and were happy once again.

But from then on, the name of Loki became a symbol of evil and dishonor among the dwellers in Asgard.

Baldur the Beautiful

THE TREACHERY OF LOKI

BALDUR was the son of Frigga, the Queen of the Norse gods. Baldur was the most beautiful of the gods, and he was also gentle, fair and wise. Wherever he went, people were happy just at the sight of him. He was not only the favorite of his mother, but the favorite of all the other gods.

One night, Baldur dreamed three dreams. Each dream was more sad and terrible than the one before it. In the third of his dreams, he found himself in a dark and lonely place. He heard a sad voice cry, "The sun is gone! The spring is gone! Joy is gone! For Baldur, the beautiful, is dead!"

The young god was very much upset. He told his lovely young wife, Nanna, about these sad and terrifying dreams. Nanna ran weeping to Queen Frigga saying, "Oh, mother, this must not come true!" Queen Frigga was deeply frightened. But she spoke soothingly to the young wife and said, "Do not fear, Nanna. Baldur is so dear to all the world, how could there be anything in the world that would hurt him?"

But Queen Frigga was heavy-hearted. The dream had fright-ened her.

She thought of a plan. "I will travel all over the heavens and all over the earth," she said. "I will make all things promise not to hurt my boy."

First, she went to the gods themselves. She told them of Baldur's dreams. She implored them to promise that none of them would ever harm Baldur. They all promised gladly.

Then Frigga traveled all over the world step by step. From all things, she got the same promise. From the trees and the plants; from the stones and the metals; from earth, air, fire and water; from sun, snow, wind and rain; and from all the diseases that men know —every creature and every thing promised not to harm Baldur.

At last, the weary but joyful Queen returned to Asgard, home of the gods. Frigga brought happy news: there was nothing in the world that would hurt Baldur. And there was great rejoicing in Asgard. All the gods felt relieved. They became quite gay. When someone suggested that they play a game which would prove how wrong the dream was, everyone agreed.

They placed Baldur at one end of the field. He stood there in all his golden beauty, his face glowing with a bright light like that of the sun. And as he stood there unarmed and smiling, the other gods took turns shooting arrows at him, hurling their spears against him, throwing sticks and stones. It was a jolly game, for every stone fell harmless at Baldur's feet; each arrow and spear turned aside as it reached his body. Baldur stood serene and smiling while the missiles piled up around him. Nothing would hurt him.

But among the crowd that stood watching and playing, there was one who did not smile. Loki the crafty one, Loki the evil one, did not laugh and cheer like the others. Loki was filled with jealous anger and malice. Baldur had never done him any harm, yet Loki hated him; for Loki knew full well that no one in the world loved him in the same way they loved Baldur. An evil plan took shape in Loki's mind. While the others were engaged in the happy game, Loki disguised himself as an old woman, and made his way to the place where Queen Frigga was sitting.

"Good day, my lady," he said. "What is all that noise and excitement over yonder in the field?"

"Don't you know?" answered Queen Frigga in surprise. "They are shooting at my son, Baldur. They are proving the promise that every creature and every thing has made, not to injure my beloved son. You see, the promise is being kept."

The old woman pretended to be very much surprised. "Really!" she cried. "Do you mean to say that every single thing in the whole world has promised not to hurt Baldur? It is true that he is a fine fellow, but still that is a remarkable thing. Have you gotten such a promise from absolutely everything in the world?"

"Oh, yes," said Queen Frigga, "everything has promised. Of course, there is one tiny little plant so small and unimportant that I did not even bother to ask."

"And what little plant is that?" said the old woman.

"It is the mistletoe that grows nearby. It is really too harmless to bother with," said Frigga.

Loki hobbled away, but as soon as he saw that no one was noticing him, he picked up his gown and ran as fast as he could to the spot where the little mistletoe grew. Then he took out his knife and cut off a piece of mistletoe. With the same knife, Loki whittled the mistletoe and trimmed it and shaped it until it was a slender arrow. Then he hobbled back to the field where the merry game was still going on. In one corner of the field stood Hod, the blind brother of Baldur. Loki, still in the guise of an old woman, tapped his arm. "Why are you not taking part in the merry game?" she asked. "They all do honor to your brother. Surely you ought to do so, too."

Then Hod touched his sightless eyes. "Ah," he said, "I am blind. How I would rejoice to give honor to my dear brother but I cannot see to aim a weapon."

"You ought to at least throw a little stick," said the old woman. "Here is a little green twig that you can use as a dart. I will guide your arm while you throw it."

Hod smiled with pleasure and stretched forth his arm eagerly. Then Loki placed the arrow of mistletoe in Hod's hand and taking careful aim, hurled it straight at Baldur's heart. With a cry, Baldur fell forward on the grass. Everyone rushed forward. They could not understand what had happened. When they saw that Baldur was dead, they knew that it was the end of sunshine and spring and joy in Asgard. The terrible dream had come true!

Then they turned upon Hod ready to tear him to pieces. "What is it! What have I done?" asked the poor blind brother.

"What have you done? You have slain Baldur!" they cried.

"No! No!" cried Hod. "I could never have done such a thing. It was the old woman, the evil old woman, who stood at my elbow and gave me a little twig to throw. She must be a witch."

The gods scattered all over the field to look for the old woman, but she had mysteriously disappeared. Then they noticed that Loki was not amongst them. "It must have been Loki!" they said.

The heartbroken gods placed Baldur on a beautiful ship to send him to Queen Hela, the queen of Death. And weeping and wailing, they sent him on his way. But Queen Frigga sent a message to Queen Hela to find out if there was not some way to win back Baldur from the kingdom of Death.

"I would let him go if I might," Queen Hela said, "but a queen cannot always do as she likes. There is only one way that you can bring Baldur back to life. If everything upon earth will weep for Baldur's death, then he may return. But should even one creature fail to weep, Baldur must remain with me."

The gods sent messages all over the world bidding every creature to weep for Baldur's death. There seemed to be little need for such a message, for already there was weeping and mourning in every part of the world. Even the giants, who were enemies of the gods, wept for Baldur. It began to look as though Baldur might be ransomed from Death.

But when all the messengers returned to Asgard, one of them told that he had found an ugly old giantess in a deep, black cave who refused to weep for Baldur. The messenger had begged her to weep but the giantess had answered, "Baldur is nothing to me. I care not whether he lives or dies." So all the tears of the sorrowing world were useless, because one creature would not weep.

Then the gods knew who the old woman was. It could be no one but Loki. "Loki has done his last evil deed," shouted Thor the Thunderer, as he lifted his mighty hammer. "Come, my brothers," Thor cried, "we have wept long enough. It is now time to punish!"

Loki tried to escape by changing himself into a fish, and hiding in a deep river. "They'll never be able to find me here," he said.

But although Odin, the All-Father, had only one eye, he could see everything in the world. He could see through thick mountains and down into the deepest sea. Odin took a net and scooped Loki out of the river. When he grasped Loki's slippery fish body, Loki was changed back into his own shape. There he stood, surrounded by the wrathful gods.

"Kill him! Kill him!" they shouted, as Odin pushed him along the road to Asgard. And on the way to the rainbow bridge which led from Asgard to Midgard, the land of the humans, thousands of men lined the road shouting, "Kill him! Kill him!"

From their caverns in the mountains came the dwarfs. They stood shaking their fists at Loki. The beasts growled and bared their

"I will guide your arm while you throw it."

fangs as if they wished to tear Loki into pieces; the birds flew at him trying to peck out his eyes; insects came in clouds to sting him, and serpents darted their fangs at him, ready to poison him with their deadly bite. But Odin decided on an even worse punishment than death. He led Loki down into a damp, dark cave under the ground where sunlight never came. The cave was full of ugly toads and snakes. In this terrible prison chamber, Loki was placed upon three sharp stones. He was bound with thongs of leather; but as soon as the leather bands were fastened to him, they turned into iron bands, so that no one, though he might have the strength of a giant, could ever loosen them. These bands cut into Loki as he lay.

Over his head was hung a venomous serpent. From its mouth, poison which burned and stung like fire, dropped into Loki's face.

Everybody in the world hated Loki except one. In spite of all his wickedness, Loki's wife, Sigyn, remained faithful to him. She stood by his head and held a bowl to catch the poison which dropped from the serpent's jaw, so that it would not reach Loki's face. But whenever the bowl became full, Sigyn had to take it away to empty it and then the burning, horrible drops of poison fell on Loki's face.

Under the caverns, Loki still lies, struggling to be free. When the poison falls upon his face, he shrieks and struggles so violently that the whole earth trembles. Then people cry, "An earthquake!" and they run away as fast as they can. For Loki, the evil one, though bound, is still dangerous. And bound as he is, Loki will stay imprisoned until the end of the world.

The Story of Aladdin

THE WONDERFUL LAMP

ALADDIN was a poor boy who lived with his widowed mother. His father, a tailor, had died, and his mother had to work long and hard to support them both. For years, they lived in great poverty.

When Aladdin was about fifteen years old, he was playing in the streets. An old man came up to him and asked:

"Are you not the son of Mustapha, the tailor?"

"Yes, sir," said Aladdin, "but my father has been dead these many years."

At this the old man began to weep and sigh. "Alas!" he cried. "This is sad news indeed. I am your father's brother. I have been away for many years, traveling all over the world. Now, at last, I have returned, yearning to see my brother once more, only to hear that he is dead. Oh, woe is me!"

Then he asked Aladdin about his mother. Upon hearing that she was very poor, he gave Aladdin three pieces of gold and said, "Here, my boy, take this money. Go home and tell your mother that I will come to your house tonight."

Aladdin ran home with the three pieces of gold and told his mother the story. His mother was astonished, for her husband had never spoken of a brother. But she took the gold and bought everything needed to make a fine dinner for her guest.

That evening, the man came to Aladdin's house, as he had promised.

"You are now my family," he said to Aladdin and his mother, "and I want to help you in every way. I have become rich, and I have no one to lavish my wealth on except you. Aladdin shall be like my own son. Tomorrow morning I will take him to the shops and buy him some new clothing. Then we will see the sights of the city."

Aladdin and his mother could hardly believe their good fortune; it was hard to imagine that Aladdin's father had had such a kind brother and had never even mentioned him to his wife. But early the next morning, the old man appeared to take Aladdin to the market place.

Sure enough, he bought him a suit of beautiful clothes. Then he bought him sweetmeats, and together they walked around the bazaars, admiring the beautiful things for sale there.

But in a short time the old man said, "I am tired of all the noise and din of the city. Let us walk a little distance away where we can sit and rest under the trees."

Thereupon, he led Aladdin to a lonely spot outside the city. No sooner had they seated themselves under a tree to rest, than the old man took some powder out of his sleeve and threw it on the ground, muttering mysterious words.

Suddenly, there was a terrible noise, and the earth opened up. Aladdin was exceedingly frightened. Now he realized that the stranger was not his uncle at all. He was a magician!

Aladdin started to run away, but the old man gave him a severe blow and said, "Lazy boy, do as I tell you!"

Quaking with fear, Aladdin said, "I will do anything you say!"

Now, in the magic opening in the earth, a few steps could be seen, and a little farther down there was a flat rock with a metal ring in it. The magician went over to the stone and, holding the ring, lifted up the rock with great ease, as if it were a trap door. Beneath the rock were more steps.

"Listen carefully to what I tell you," he said to Aladdin. "You will go down these steps. They will lead you into a large cavern containing three rooms. Walk straight through all the rooms. Do not touch a thing you see, or you will die instantly. The third room leads out to a beautiful garden. In a corner of the garden, on a stone table, you will see a lamp. Take the lamp and place it in your blouse. Then come right back to me. Be sure that you do not touch anything else you see, or you will die. Here, put this ring on your finger, for without it you could not set foot in the cavern at all. Go, and come back quickly."

Aladdin did as he was told. When he had descended the steps, he found himself in an enormous underground room. It was hung with gorgeous silks. Soft rugs covered the floor. There were beautiful chairs strewn with velvet cushions, and tables inlaid with mother-of-pearl. But the thing that made him open his eyes wide in excitement was this: on all the tables there were big bowls full of gold and precious stones. Oh, how he yearned to fill his pockets! But he remembered what he had been told, and he dared not touch a thing.

He walked into the next room, which was even more dazzling than the first! The third room exceeded even the second in splendor, but Aladdin touched not a thing. When he reached the garden, there, as the magician had said, was a stone table, and on it was an old lamp. It was very ordinary looking, like the things that Aladdin saw every day.

"I wonder why the magician wants only this lamp, when there is so much gold and so many precious stones down here?" he thought. But he tucked the lamp well down inside his blouse and went back.

As he came near the top of the steps, the magician called out, "Did you get the lamp?"

"Yes," said Aladdin.

"Then come up here and hand it to me," said the magician.

"I will indeed," said Aladdin, "but the steps are very narrow and steep here. Will you give me your hand to help me?"

"Give me the lamp first," said the magician.

"It is far down in my blouse and I cannot reach it," said Aladdin. "If you will help me up I will give it to you."

"No!" said the magician. "First hand me the lamp!"

But Aladdin could not let go of the walls of the staircase to give him the lamp. This threw the magician into a rage. He threw some of his magic powder over the spot, shouted his magic words, and the next moment the stone had returned to its place!

Aladdin found himself in complete darkness. He was buried alive! He wept and called to the magician that he would give him the lamp, to please let him out. But no one answered his cries; everything was still and black as night.

At last, Aladdin gave up calling. He felt his way down the steep stairs, thinking that he would go out into the garden. But when he came to the bottom of the steps, the door leading to the three rooms was closed. Aladdin felt all around him, but found nothing except stone walls. Then he sat down on the steps and wept. After a while he decided to pray.

As he clasped his hands together, his finger rubbed against the magic ring which the magician had given him. Instantly, his dark prison was lit up with glowing light as a huge genie rose before him.

"What do you wish, oh master?" said the genie. "I am your slave."

"Who are you?" cried Aladdin, quaking with fear.

"I am the genie of the ring. I am the slave of him who wears

. . . a huge genie rose before him.

the ring on his finger. Command me, and it shall be done," said the genie.

"Get me out of this place," cried Aladdin.

Scarcely had the words left his mouth, than he found himself on the surface of the earth once more, on the same spot where he had stood with the magician. The genie was gone.

Aladdin rose to his feet, trembling, and made his way back to his home. He told his mother all that had happened, and she wept with joy at his escape.

When Aladdin awoke the next morning, he was very hungry and asked for something to eat.

"Alas, my son," answered his mother, "there is not a morsel of food left in the house. I do not have anything left to sell for food. But what of that lamp which you brought home with you? Maybe, if I polished it up somewhat, I could sell it for a few pennies."

"That's a good idea," said Aladdin.

So his mother got a piece of soft cloth and started to rub the dusty lamp. But no sooner had she rubbed the cloth once over the lamp, than an enormous genie appeared before them.

"Command, and I obey," he said. "I am the genie of the lamp."

Aladdin's mother stood cowering in fear. But Aladdin said, "Bring us food."

The genie disappeared. In a few moments he returned, carrying a silver tray loaded with food in dishes of silver. He placed them all on the table and again disappeared.

From that time, Aladdin and his mother had everything they wished. But they told no one of the source of their good fortune.

One day, when Aladdin was walking in the city, he heard two of the Sultan's criers going through the town, ordering everyone to go indoors. Aladdin asked the reason for this. He was told that the Sultan's daughter was returning from the baths, and it was not proper for anyone to see her.

Aladdin hid himself behind a door, where he could look without being seen, for he was curious to get a glimpse of the princess. Just as she and her attendants passed by the place where Aladdin was hiding, the princess lifted her veil. She was so beautiful that Aladdin fell deeply in love with her, and determined to marry her.

He went home and called upon the genie of the lamp. He ordered him to provide a troop of servants, gorgeous clothes, and magnificent gifts. Then, Aladdin presented himself before the Sultan to ask for the hand of his daughter.

"Who are you to be courting my daughter?" said the Sultan. "Don't you know that the princess has been wooed by the richest men in the country?"

"Whatever wealth they offer her," answered Aladdin, "I will offer more. Ask for anything you want, and I will provide it!"

When the Sultan heard these words, he was sure that Aladdin was boasting. "We will soon see," he thought to himself. Then he said, "I want my daughter to have a palace even more magnificent than my own, with one hundred slaves and one hundred bags of gold."

"Where do you want the palace to stand?" asked Aladdin.

The Sultan laughed and said, "On the great plain just outside of the city."

"Make the preparations for the wedding," replied Aladdin, "for you have not long to wait."

The next morning the Sultan, the court, and all the people of the city were astonished to see an enormous and beautiful palace standing on the plain outside of the city. It was complete in every detail. There were beautiful furnishings, gorgeous gardens, horses in the stables, and a hundred servants ready to do their master's bidding.

When the Sultan saw this marvel, he sent a message to Aladdin, saying, "I gladly give my consent to the marriage. It shall be held this very day."

So Aladdin married the beautiful princess, and he was the happiest man in the world.

But his happiness was short-lived, for soon a disaster befell him. His old enemy, the wicked magician, found out by his arts that Aladdin had the magic lamp. He was furious, and he plotted and planned to get it for himself.

One day, when Aladdin was hunting, an old peddler appeared in the women's courtyard of Aladdin's palace. His presence caused great excitement, for he offered a most unusual bargain.

"New lamps for old! New lamps for old!" he called.

"That's foolish!" said the servants. "He cannot mean what he says. Come, let us see if he will stick to his offer."

One of the servants remembered having seen an old lamp high up in a cupboard. She ran and brought it to the peddler. "Here," she said, "now give me one of your shiny, new lamps for this."

The peddler, who was really the magician in disguise, knew at once that the old lamp was none other than the wonderful magic lamp. He gave the servant a new lamp and took the magic lamp in its place. With a chortle of glee he rubbed it, and the next moment, according to his wish, the whole palace, with everyone in it, was transported to a distant country.

The grief of the Sultan was terrible when he saw that his daughter had disappeared. When Aladdin returned from hunting, the Sultan said, "If you do not bring back my daughter within forty days, you shall be beheaded!"

He did not have to threaten Aladdin with so dire a punishment, for Aladdin was as heartbroken as he. Then Aladdin remembered the magic ring, which he still wore on his finger. He rubbed it and commanded the genie of the ring to transport him to the place where his palace now stood. Instantly, Aladdin found himself in the garden of his palace, beneath the window of his wife's room. The princess, who had been sitting and weeping, caught sight of her beloved husband. Quickly, she got up, and putting her finger to her lips, cautioned Aladdin to be careful. Then she sent a servant to lead him into the palace by a secret door.

After kissing his wife fondly, Aladdin asked her what had become of the old lamp which he had kept on the shelf. She told him what had happened.

"And now," she said, "the ugly old magician wants to make me his wife, for he told me that I would never see you or my homeland again. He carries the magic lamp in his blouse and never parts from it."

Then Aladdin made a plan to overcome the magician. He had the princess prepare two goblets of wine. Into one of them he put a powder which was so deadly that anyone drinking of that goblet would die instantly. Then he had the princess invite the magician to sup with her. No sooner had the magician taken one sip of the poisoned wine, than he fell down dead. Aladdin, who was hiding behind a curtain, then ran forward and took the lamp from the magician's blouse. He called the genie, who instantly transported the palace back to where it had stood before.

The Sultan arose the next morning and, looking out the window, saw the beautiful palace gleaming in the sun. Oh, what rejoicing there was in the city!

Now the wicked magician was dead, and Aladdin and his wife lived happily ever after.

The Story of Sindbad
the Sailor

THREE SEA ADVENTURES

IN the city of Bagdad, there once lived a poor porter by the name of Hindbad. He had to work long and hard, carrying heavy bundles, in order to get enough money just for food.

One day, as he was walking along a strange street, he saw a magnificent house. He was so tired that he sat down and leaned against the wall to rest. Wondering who lived in so fine a house, he asked one of the servants standing at the gate. The servant answered that it was the home of Sindbad the Sailor.

"Oh," cried Hindbad, "how unjust the world is! Why should I be sitting out here in rags and tatters, with an empty belly, while Sindbad feasts himself and lives in luxury?"

Now it happened that just at that moment, Sindbad himself had come to the gate. He overheard poor Hindbad's remark.

"My good man," he said, "come with me." And he led him into a great hall where a sumptuous meal was spread before him.

When Hindbad had eaten, beautiful maidens entertained them with dancing and singing. Hindbad was overcome by Sindbad's kindness.

"My lord," he said to Sindbad, "please forgive me for what I said. I was tired and hungry, and I did not know what a good man you are."

"I forgive you," said Sindbad, "but in order to show you that I did not gain this wealth easily, I shall tell you the story of my travels."

Thereupon Sindbad began:

"When I was still a very young man, I inherited a large fortune from my father. But instead of acting wisely, I spent my money on pleasures and luxuries; and, before very long, I discovered that I was almost penniless. Seeing myself faced with poverty, I bought some merchandise with the little money I had left, and set sail on a ship bound for the Indies, hoping to make back my fortune by selling the goods.

"One day, my ship was becalmed near a small, treeless island. Having the captain's permission, I rowed ashore with a small group of men.

"Pleased to be on dry land again, we built a fire, in order to cook our lunch. But no sooner had the flames started to rise, than the island began to tremble violently. Imagine our horror when we discovered that what we had mistaken for an island was the back of a huge whale!

"The fire on its back had angered the monster, and before we knew what was happening, the angry beast had dived into the depths. Everyone was drowned except myself. I had the good fortune to grasp a log of wood which kept me afloat.

"In the turmoil, the ship was carried far away from me. I called and called, but in vain, for no one on the ship could hear me. The captain was certain that everyone on the 'island' had been drowned, so he hoisted sail and sailed away from the fateful spot as fast as he could.

"In despair, I gave myself up for lost. I was clinging to the log with my last strength, when, by a great piece of good luck, I was thrown against an island. Thanking God for my rescue, I got to my feet and struggled up the bank to the nearby woods to look around.

"Suddenly, I heard some voices, and a man called out to me: 'Who are you? And where do you come from?' I looked up, and there was a group of men standing close by. Overjoyed to see human beings again, I told them who I was and what had happened to me. They were so amazed at the marvelous adventure that they told me they would bring me before their king so that I could tell him my story. They also told me that if I had been washed ashore just a few hours later, they would have been gone, and I never would have been able to find my way to the city alone.

"When the king heard my story, he was so entranced that he invited me to stay with him as long as I wished. He provided me with every comfort and luxury, but I still longed to return to my own land.

"One day, as I was visiting the port, what was my astonishment when I saw the very ship from which I had been separated, enter the port! As I stood there dumbfounded, I saw the porters unloading bales with my own name upon them. I went straight to the captain and told him who I was.

"At first, the captain insisted that I could not be Sindbad, that he had seen Sindbad perish before his eyes; but I finally convinced him of who I was. Then I chose the most beautiful and valuable things from amongst my goods and presented them to the king who had treated me so generously. He was highly pleased with my gifts, and he gave me even more valuable presents in return.

"Thus, I set sail upon the same ship and, after selling my merchandise at various ports along the way, returned to my city a rich man once more."

Sindbad finished his story here, and, as Hindbad was marveling at it, he presented him with a bag of gold and said, "Take this, Hindbad, and come back tomorrow night to hear more of my adventures."

The next night, Sindbad told the story of his second voyage.

"I had intended, after my first voyage," he began, "to spend the rest of my days here in Bagdad. But I soon grew tired of such a quiet life. Once more, I bought merchandise and placed it on a ship, and once more I set forth with the ship.

"One day, we caught sight of an island which seemed to be

covered with all sorts of fruit trees, but we could see neither man nor animal. However, we were delighted at the chance to walk in the lovely meadows, so a large group of us prepared some baskets of food and landed. I chose a spot beneath a large, shady tree, and, after walking a bit, I sat down to drink. It was so pleasant beneath the tree that I soon fell asleep.

"I cannot tell how long I slept, but when I awoke, the ship and all my companions were gone. There I was, all alone on a deserted island. Not knowing what to do, I climbed to the top of the tree to see if I could discover anything. As I gazed over the island, I saw what looked like a large, white dome. Hoping that it might be a castle or a house, I gathered up my provisions and went toward it. But as I drew near, I saw that it had neither doors nor windows. It was just a large, white, smooth object, with curved sides, like an immense egg.

"Suddenly, as I stood there, the sky became dark, as if it had been covered with a thick cloud. I looked up. The most enormous bird I had ever seen was flying toward me. In terror, I huddled against the white dome. Then I remembered that I had often heard mariners speak of a gigantic bird called 'the roc.' This, then, must be the bird of which they spoke, and this enormous white object was, indeed, an egg — the roc's egg!

"The bird alighted and sat over the egg. Then an idea came to me. Why couldn't the roc carry me away from this lonely island? So I tied myself to the leg of the bird with my turban, and in this fashion I spent the night. In the morning, the enormous bird rose to fly away, carrying me with her.

"She flew so high that I could hardly see the earth beneath me, and I closed my eyes in terror. Soon afterward, she descended with such speed that I lost my senses. But when the roc came to rest on the ground, I recovered and quickly untied the turban from her leg. The next moment, the roc had flown away.

"I looked about and discovered that the place where the roc had left me was a deep valley. On all sides rose tremendous cliffs. As I looked around, a marvelous sight met my eyes. All over the ground lay thousands of diamonds! My heart thumped with excitement.

"The next moment, my joy was turned to terror, for a short distance away I saw a great number of serpents, so huge that the smallest of them was capable of swallowing an elephant. But fortunately, they all seemed to be asleep. Then I realized that, during the day, these serpents hid amongst the rocks to escape from their enemy, the giant roc. But in the nighttime, when they were safe, they came out of their hiding places. Seeing that it would soon be night, I hid myself in a cave and closed up its mouth with a pile of stones. But all night long I heard the hissing of the serpents outside, and I could not close my eyes for fear.

"When morning came, the serpents went into their hiding places, and I came out of the cave. I ate the last of my provisions. Now I was in despair. How could I escape from this fearful valley?

Of what use to me was the enormous wealth that lay about my feet? Suddenly, I heard a loud noise near me. I started up. Then I saw a large piece of raw meat lying on the ground. At the same moment, I saw several other pieces of meat fall down from the cliffs in different places. Then I remembered a story I had heard from the sailors — that there was a valley filled with diamonds and enormous serpents. Merchants would come to the tops of the cliffs around the valley, at the time of the year when eagles have their young. The merchants would throw great chunks of meat into the valley. The loose diamonds would stick to the meat. Then the eagles would fly down and pick up the meat to carry it to their young in their nests, high up in the cliffs. The merchants then ran to the nests and, driving off the eagles with their shouts, would take the diamonds which stuck to the meat.

"Here was hope for my escape! First I collected the largest and most beautiful diamonds that I could find. I filled my pockets with them. Then I tied one of the pieces of meat to my back and lay down with my face to the ground.

"In a few moments, a large eagle came. He grasped the meat in his powerful claws and carried me up out of the valley of diamonds to his nest on the top of the mountain. No sooner had I been placed in the nest, than a merchant came shouting and waving a stick. I told him to help me out quickly, leaving the meat in the nest. He did so.

" 'Here,' I said. 'You saved my life. I have more than enough

" . . . *the enormous bird rose to fly away, carrying me with her.*"

diamonds for you and myself. I will divide what I have with you, and you will be rich for the rest of your life.'

"The merchant answered, 'I am glad that your life was saved. As for sharing your diamonds with you, I do not desire to be so rich. Give me just one of the largest, and I will be more than happy.'

"This I did gladly. The merchant then led me to a nearby port where I took a ship for home. When at length I reached home, I gave large presents to the poor, in gratitude for my rescue. Now I was richer than ever, and I was determined to live happily and contentedly."

Thus ended the story of Sindbad's second voyage. He gave Hindbad another bag of gold and invited him to come again the next night, to hear more of his adventures.

The next night Sindbad told the following story:

"One would have thought that I would never again want to leave the safety of my home, but in a short time I became restless once more. This time, I built a ship at my own expense. I loaded it with rich cargo and, taking with me other merchants, set sail.

"One day, we struck a terrible storm. We thought that we would surely be drowned, but, luckily, we were able to land on a desert island. The storm subsided, and we looked about to find fresh water. Instead, we found a roc's egg, even larger than the one I had seen on my second voyage.

"The merchants and sailors gathered about it, and although I advised them not to hurt it, nothing could stop them. Using picks and shovels, they made a large hole in it, and picked out the young roc which was soon to be hatched. They then roasted it and ate it.

"They had scarcely finished their meal when two enormous rocs appeared in the air. We quickly rushed to our ship and set sail, but the huge birds, enraged at the destruction of their young, flew at us. One of them picked up an immense rock in his claws and, flying directly over the ship, let it fall.

"The ship was split in two. I did not know what happened to the others of the crew, but I clung to a fragment of the ship and so saved my life.

"In a few hours, the wind and waves bore me to another island. I hurried up the beach. Soon I found that the island was full of the finest fruit trees, and had excellent water. As I was sitting near a little stream, blessing my good fortune, a feeble old man came toward me. I greeted him, and he asked me to carry him over the stream so that he might eat some fruit. Seeing no harm in this, I motioned him to get on my back, and knelt down to make it easier for him. But instead of clasping his legs around my waist, he sat on my shoulders and clasped his legs around my throat so tightly that I thought he would strangle me. I fainted with pain and fright.

"When I came to, the old fellow was still sitting on my back. He made me rise up and walk under the trees so that he could gather the fruit at his ease. Then I saw that I was his slave and his prisoner. I could not get him off me. I seemed doomed to carry him about on my shoulders for the rest of my life.

"But a plan for escape soon occurred to me. Using a gourd for a bottle, I pressed some grape juice into it, and let it stand for a few days. In this way, I made wine. I gave some to the old man, and he drank it eagerly and asked for more. I plied him with the liquor, and soon he became intoxicated, lost his balance, and fell off my shoulders.

"I ran quickly across the island. Good fortune was with me, for there I met the crew of a ship which had stopped to take on fresh water. They told me that I had fallen into the hands of the Old Man of the Sea, and that I was the first person ever to have escaped. They took me on board with them and we sailed away.

"On the way home, we stopped at an island where there were many coconut trees. I gathered a large number of coconuts. Since coconuts were a rarity in my native land, I sold them for a large amount of money. I retired once more to the comfort of my home, and determined never more to leave its safety and ease."

Thus ended the story of the last adventure of Sindbad the Sailor.

Ali Baba and the Forty Thieves

HOW CLEVER ROBBERS WERE OUTSMARTED

IN Persia, there once lived two brothers named Cassim and Ali Baba. Cassim was a rich man, but Ali Baba was poor. He earned his living by cutting wood in the forest.

One day, when Ali Baba was in the forest as usual and had just finished loading his donkey with logs, he saw a great cloud of dust in the distance. A troop of horsemen was approaching. Fearing that they might be a band of robbers, Ali Baba hid his donkey in the bushes and quickly climbed a tree. As he sat hidden among the branches, he watched the horsemen coming nearer and nearer. Imagine his surprise when they stopped right beneath the tree in which he was hiding!

They were all armed with knives, and there was no doubt that they were robbers. Ali Baba counted forty of them. They got off their horses and proceeded to unload bags of gold from the horses' backs.

The captain stood facing a large rock which was near the roots of the tree. He called out *"Open Sesame!"* At this, a door in the rock opened. All the robbers passed in, the captain last of all. Ali Baba heard the captain say, *"Close Sesame!"* Then, the door closed.

Ali Baba sat there trembling. He was afraid to come down from the tree for fear of being seen. And, indeed, in a short while, the door in the rock opened once more, and all the thieves came out, this time without the bags of gold. The captain called out *"Close Sesame!"* and the door closed. Then the thieves rode off.

Ali Baba watched until they were far away in the distance. Then he climbed down from the tree. He stood before the rock and said, *"Open Sesame!"* Sure enough, the door opened. He walked in. What a sight met his eyes! Chests of gold lay everywhere. Robes of silk and velvet shimmered from the walls. Caskets of precious stones sparkled wherever he looked. This was where the robbers hid their treasure.

Quickly, Ali Baba loaded his donkey with as many bags of gold as the beast could carry. Then he threw his cloak over the bags to hide them. He stood outside the cave and called out *"Close Sesame!"* and the door closed behind him.

He hurried home and told his wife what had happened. She was both frightened and overjoyed, for now they were rich.

"We must be very careful not to let people know that we have become rich so suddenly," she said, "for the robbers might hear of our wealth and guess where we got it."

"You are wise, good wife," said Ali Baba. "Let us use only a little bit of the gold and hide the rest."

"Yes," said his wife, "but I must know how much we have. There is so much I could never count every piece. I do not have a measuring cup, so tomorrow I shall borrow the large corn measure from your brother's wife and see how much gold we have."

The next day she ran to her sister-in-law's house and asked to borrow her corn measure. Now Cassim's wife knew how poor Ali Baba was, and she wondered what kind of grain Ali Baba's wife was going to measure. She put a little candle wax at the bottom of the cup so that some of the grain would stick to it.

When Ali Baba's wife returned the measure, Cassim's wife looked to see what might have stuck to the bottom. What was her surprise when she saw a piece of gold there!

When her husband came home she said, "Cassim, you think that you are rich; but see, your brother has become so rich that he does not count his gold piece by piece, as you do—oh, no, he measures it with a corn measure!"

The rich Cassim, far from being happy at this, was jealous. He went to Ali Baba and said, "Ali Baba, you pretend to be poor, but really you are rich. Is that the way to act toward your own brother?"

Then Ali Baba told him everything that had happened. He told him the magic words that opened the cave. Being kind and generous, Ali Baba offered to divide all the treasure with him.

"That is no more than I expect," said Cassim. Then he left

for his home.

But early the next morning he got up. He got ready ten mules and tied a pair of empty hampers on each of their backs. Then he set forth for the robbers' cave, planning to take all the treasure for himself.

When he got to the cave, he called out *"Open Sesame!"* and went in. He feasted his eyes on the magnificent treasure. Then he cried, *"Close Sesame!"* and set to work filling the hampers with it. It took him all morning and part of the afternoon to load his ten mules, for he could not bear to leave anything behind. Finally, he was finished. But when it was time to leave the cave, he could not remember the words he had to say to make the door open. He thought and thought, but he could not remember the word *"Sesame"*.

While he was in the cave the robbers returned. The captain called out *"Open Sesame!"* and the door opened. There they found Cassim in the act of stealing their treasure. They killed him on the spot.

Then the captain said, "It is clear that the magic words which open this cave are known. But we will teach a lesson to anyone else who might try to steal our treasure."

So saying, he ordered the men to cut up Cassim's body and hang the pieces in the front of the cave. Then they all left the place.

Now, when Cassim did not return home after a day and a night had passed, his wife became frightened. She went to Ali Baba and said, "I do not know what has happened to Cassim. He went to the robbers' cave yesterday, and he has not returned. I fear some evil has befallen him."

As soon as Ali Baba heard this, he saddled three mules and set forth for the cave. When the door opened, he was struck with horror at the sight that met him. He took down the quartered body of his brother and placed it on one donkey. Then he covered up the body with sticks. Next, he loaded the other two donkeys with bags of gold, and he covered the bags with sticks and logs. Then he left the cave and closed the door.

He hid in the forest until night. Under cover of the dark, he made his way back to his house. He told his wife the terrible story. Then he gave her one of the donkeys which was laden with gold, to unload, while he went to his brother's house with the other donkey and his brother's body.

The door of his brother's house was opened by their beautiful maidservant, Morgiana. This slave was not only beautiful; she was also very clever and brave. When Ali Baba told her what had happened, she said, "Oh, my poor master! My poor mistress!" Then she went to her mistress.

She told her what had happened, but she warned her that they must make it seem as if Cassim had died a natural death.

"Fear not, dear mistress," she said. "Leave everything to me."

Then she went to the outskirts of the town to an old shoemaker.

"Old man," she said, "would you like to earn five pieces of gold? If you do what I say, that is what I will give you."

At first, the shoemaker was frightened, for he suspected that she wanted him to do something wrong. But when he saw the money, he agreed.

Morgiana then blindfolded the shoemaker so that he should not know where he was being taken, and she led him to Cassim's house. She showed him the body and told him to sew it together, which he did. Then she paid him the gold, blindfolded him once more, and led him back to his shop. The next day, she let it be known that Cassim was very sick.

Only after all this had been done did she allow her mistress to make an outcry of grief, and wail and cry that her husband had died. In this way, no one in the town knew anything, except that Cassim had taken sick suddenly and had died.

Ali Baba then gave his sister-in-law the other donkey laden with gold so that she should not be left penniless, and he and his wife went to live with her.

Now, when the robbers returned to the cave and found the body gone, and more gold taken, they realized that more than one person knew their secret.

"We must find the one who knows our hiding place, else we are ruined," said the captain.

He ordered his men to disguise themselves and spread out in the town to find out what they could. He, too, disguised himself as a merchant and entered the town. As luck would have it, the first place he entered was the shoemaker's shop—the very shoemaker who had sewn Cassim's body together.

"Good evening, old man," said the robber captain. "It is almost night, and yet you are still at work. How can you see to sew at this hour?"

Then the shoemaker answered, "These old eyes of mine are better than most people's, even those who are half my age. Why, the other night I was called upon to do a piece of work which I daresay no man has ever done before. Yet I did it so well that no one even saw the stitches."

"And what could that be?" asked the robber.

"I sewed a man's body together. That's what I did!" answered the old shoemaker.

At this, the robber's ears opened. "Can it be possible," he thought, "that already I have found the man who can lead me to the right place? I'm in luck, all right!"

Then he asked the shoemaker to show him where he had done the deed. But the old man told him that he had been blindfolded and did not know where the house was. The robber said, "I will blindfold you again. Do just what you did before, and maybe you will find the place."

The old man shrugged his shoulders. "I doubt that I can find it, but if you are willing to pay me in any case, I will go."

"Done," said the robber. And they set forth. The old man, following the path that he had taken a few days before, led the robber right to Cassim's house.

"I think this is it," he said.

Then the robber made a chalk mark on the door, and they went away.

The next morning, however, when Morgiana, the maidservant, was coming back from the market, she noticed the chalk mark on the door. "I know not what this means," she said to herself, "but I do not like it." So she got a piece of chalk and marked all the houses on the street in the same way.

That evening, the robber returned with all his men. But since all the houses were marked in the same way, he did not know which was the one he wanted. In a rage, he was forced to go away.

Once more he had to pay the shoemaker to lead him to the house. But this time he made no mark. Instead, he looked long and carefully at the house, until he knew it well. Then he gathered his men around him and said, "Listen carefully to my plan. We are dealing with a clever person, and we must act cleverly, too. You must follow my instructions exactly. Only then will we succeed in wreaking vengeance on this man and regain our treasure."

Then he tied forty large oil jars on the backs of twenty mules. Into each of the jars, but one, went a robber, armed with a knife. The last jar was filled with oil.

Then the robber chief dressed himself as an oil merchant. When evening came, he presented himself and his train of mules at Cassim's house.

"I am an oil merchant," he said. "I am traveling through your

Caskets of precious stones sparkled wherever he looked.

town with my merchandise, but night has overtaken me and I have no place to stay. Could you not put me and my beasts up for the night?"

Ali Baba did not recognize the robber, and he would not turn away a traveler from his door. He invited him in, and graciously offered him food and lodging and a place in his courtyard for the merchant's mules. Then he ordered Morgiana to prepare a fine meal for their guest, while he led the man to a room where he could wash and rest himself.

As Morgiana was preparing the meal, she ran out of oil. Then she remembered all the jars of oil in the courtyard and decided that, instead of disturbing their guest or her master, she would take a little oil from one of the jars. Taking her oilcan with her, she went over to one of the jars. As she drew near the huge jar, the thief who was concealed inside it whispered, "Is it the time?"

Morgiana realized in a flash what was happening. Instead of crying out in surprise, she answered in a mannish whisper, "No, not yet." Then she went on to each of the jars and spoke in the same way, until she found the jar which contained the oil.

Quickly, she returned to the house. She filled a large kettle with oil and placed it on the stove until it was boiling hot. Then, quietly, she approached each of the jars. One after another, she poured the boiling oil over each of the thieves. She did it so quickly that they did not even have a chance to make a sound, but were killed instantly.

Then Morgiana went back and served dinner to the robber-merchant and her master. When she had finished serving the meal, she dressed herself in beautiful garments, but she hid a dagger in her dress. Then she appeared once more before her master and his guest.

"I thought you would like some entertainment," she said, and she proceeded to dance for them. She twirled 'round and 'round, often bending over close to the robber, who, unaware of her plan, enjoyed himself very much.

Suddenly, Morgiana whirled around and plunged the dagger into the robber's heart.

"What have you done!" cried Ali Baba. "You have killed a guest under my own roof! Wicked girl, what is the meaning of this?"

Then Morgiana told him about the jars with the men hidden in them. Ali Baba looked again at the dead robber, and this time he recognized him.

"You have saved my life, brave girl," he said, "ask what you want; it shall be yours."

Morgiana wanted nothing, but Ali Baba gave her her freedom and a large fortune in gold. A few years later, Morgiana married Ali Baba's son and was welcomed as a daughter by Ali Baba.

The Merchant of Bagdad

HOW A BOY PRONOUNCED JUSTICE

MANY years ago, during the reign of the great Caliph Haroun-el-Rashid, there lived in Bagdad a merchant whose name was Ali Cogia. Now this merchant decided that he wanted to make a pilgrimage to Mecca, the holy city of the Mohammedans. Such a pilgrimage would take him a number of years to complete. So he sold his shop and all his merchandise, and received for them one thousand pieces of gold.

Ali Cogia then placed the thousand pieces of gold in a large, clay jar. He covered the gold with a layer of olives, and took the jar to his friend.

"My friend," he said, "I am setting forth on a pilgrimage to Mecca, and I would ask a favor of you. Will you keep this jar of olives for me until I return?"

"Gladly," answered his friend. "I will place it in my warehouse, and no one shall touch it until you return."

So Ali Cogia set forth on his pilgrimage. But instead of the journey's taking about three years, as he had expected, it lasted a period of seven years.

In the meantime, his friend had all but forgotten about him. One evening, when his friend was having supper with his wife, she happened to mention that she would like some olives.

"Now that you mention olives," said the friend, "I remind myself that Ali Cogia left a jar of olives in my warehouse to keep for him until he returned. But he has been gone so much longer than he planned, that I am sure he must be dead. Give me a plate and a candle, and I will go and fetch some olives from his jar."

"No, my husband, do not touch the property of another," said his wife. But the man refused to listen to her and went to the warehouse to get some olives.

He put his hand into the jar to pull out the olives. As he dug down, he came across a piece of gold. When he saw this, he looked further, and he found that the jar was full of money. Then he placed some of the olives on the plate and brought them back to his wife. He told her nothing about the gold, but as soon as he could, he went out and bought enough olives to fill up the whole jar. Then he emptied out the money, buried it in a secret place, and filled the jar with the olives.

When Ali Cogia returned, he called upon his friend and asked him for the jar. Ali Cogia thanked his friend for having kept it so long for him. But when he brought it home and opened it, expecting to find his money, he found nothing but olives.

Ali Cogia could hardly believe that his friend would do such a wicked thing. "Is it possible that my friend would be guilty of such a bad deed?" he thought.

He rushed back to his friend's house and said, "My friend, maybe you took my money because you were in great need. If so, I will give you time to repay me."

But the friend pretended great surprise. "What are you talking about, Ali Cogia? I know nothing about money. You gave me a jar of olives. In all these seven years I have not even gone near the jar, or so much as touched it."

This dishonest answer made Ali Cogia miserable, indeed. To lose both his money and his trust in his friend was a terrible thing.

"I see," he said in a sad voice, "that I must bring you to court to obtain justice."

"Bring me to court. Go ahead," answered his friend. "I want you to, for you have wrongfully accused me, and I insist on having my name cleared!"

So Ali Cogia brought his faithless friend to court. The judge asked if Ali Cogia had any witnesses who knew about the money. But Ali Cogia replied that he had trusted his friend so completely, he had not considered it necessary to have witnesses. Then the judge asked his friend to tell his side of the story. His friend repeated the lies that he had already told, and since there was no way of disproving what he said, the judge dismissed the case.

But Ali Cogia would not give up. "As there is a God in heaven," he cried, "I will be justified! I will bring my case to the

Sure enough, the olive merchants pronounced the olives new . .

great Caliph Haroun-el-Rashid himself. He will help me!" So Ali Cogia sent a petition, explaining the case to the Caliph.

Now it happened that on the afternoon before the Caliph was to judge Ali Cogia's case, he decided to walk through his city, disguised as an ordinary man. Haroun-el-Rashid often went among his people, disguised in this way, in order to learn what the people really thought — what their troubles were, and what they needed.

As he was walking along the street accompanied only by his most trusted attendant, he came across a group of boys who were playing a most unusual game. One boy was taking the part of a judge, while two other boys were taking the parts of Ali Cogia and his friend, for the case had become very famous throughout the city of Bagdad. As the Caliph watched, this is what he heard:

> *The pretended judge:* "And so, Ali Cogia, you say that you left this jar of gold with a layer of olives covering the gold, with your friend here, to hold for you?"
>
> *The pretended Ali Cogia:* "I did indeed, your excellency. And now he returns the jar filled only with olives and swears falsely that I left with him only a jar of olives."
>
> *The pretended judge:* "Is this true?"
>
> *The pretended friend:* "Your excellency, Ali Cogia is lying, not I. He gave me a jar of olives, and now he claims a thousand pieces of gold."
>
> *The pretended judge:* "Well now, here are two olive merchants. We will ask them a few questions. Here, sir, taste

these olives and tell me whether or not they are seven years old."

A pretended olive merchant: "Oh, no, your excellency. These olives are from this year's crop."

The pretended judge: "And you, sir. You taste them, too, and tell me what you think."

Another pretended olive merchant: "There is no doubt about it. These olives are new. They are certainly not seven years old. Anyone can see that."

The pretended judge: "Hear then the order of this court. Ali Cogia has been robbed by his false friend. Take the man away to prison!"

When Haroun-el-Rashid heard this, he asked the boy, who was pretending to be the judge, for his name. Then he said, "You are indeed a wise boy. Never have I seen such cleverness in one so young. Now, my boy, I want you to appear before Haroun-el-Rashid tomorrow morning. Do not tell anyone, but be sure to be there."

The boy did not know that it was the great Caliph himself who was speaking to him, but the next morning, when a man from the Caliph's palace came for him, he went along.

When he got there, he was astonished to see the real people in the case standing before the Caliph, ready to tell their stories. But the Caliph, who was none other than the man who had spoken to him in the street, stood up and asked the boy to stand beside him. Then the Caliph said, "Each of you plead your case before this child. He will do justice."

Everyone in the court was much astonished at this. But the Caliph had everything in readiness, including two olive merchants. The young boy repeated his words of the day before. Sure enough, the olive merchants pronounced the olives new, and not old, proving that Ali Cogia's friend had spoken falsely.

The Caliph then ordered that Ali Cogia's gold be restored to him, and that his friend be imprisoned for many years.

"As for the first judge, who judged the case so carelessly, let him learn from this child how to do his duty."

Then Haroun-el-Rashid embraced the boy and gave him a purse of one hundred pieces of gold as a token of his admiration for such wisdom and acuteness.

The Enchanted Horse

A PRINCE OUTWITS A KING

ONCE upon a time, the King of Persia was holding court, when suddenly a man dressed as a Hindu appeared before him.

"Great King," he said, "I have something here which is so wonderful that I am sure you have never seen its like in the whole world. I would like you to examine it."

At that, he brought forward an artificial horse. It looked so lifelike that for a moment everyone thought it was a real horse.

The king examined it carefully. "It is true," he said, "that your horse is marvelously wrought; but I am sure that with a little time my workmen could make one just as good or even better."

Then the Hindu replied, "But Your Majesty, did you ever see a horse that could fly through the air and carry you to any part of the world in almost no time? Well, that is what my horse can do!"

The king answered, "We will see if this is true. Do you see that high mountain in the distance? There is a palm tree on top of it. How quickly can your horse fly there and bring back to me a branch from that tree?"

"Just watch," answered the Hindu. So saying, he mounted the horse and turned a little peg on the horse's neck. The next instant, the horse and rider rose from the ground and flew like lightning toward the distant mountain. They flew so high that soon they were out of sight.

But ten minutes later the king and his court were astonished to see the horse returning with the Hindu on its back. The Hindu, triumphantly waving the palm branch in his hand, made the horse circle above the heads of the crowd three times, before bringing it down on the same spot from which he had started out.

When the king saw this, he felt that he must have the horse, no matter what the price.

"Hindu," he said, "I am king of a large and rich country. In return for this horse, I will give you one of my richest and most populous cities, for you to rule over for the rest of your life."

"Thank you, noble lord, for your great and generous offer, but do not be offended if I tell you that I do not want it. I will not be happy unless I am given your daughter as my wife."

Everyone was outraged at this bold request. The king's son, who was standing nearby, was ready to fall upon the Hindu, so great was his anger. But the king said, "My son, I am pleased to see how proud you are of the honor of your family, but calm yourself a moment and consider the situation. If we do not get this marvelous horse, the Hindu might very well sell it to someone else. Think what an advantage such a horse would be to one of our enemies. I wish that you would test the horse and find out if it will do for us what it does for the Hindu."

When the king's son heard this, he quickly mounted the horse. Without waiting for the Hindu to give him any instructions, he pulled the peg which he had seen the Hindu pull. Instantly, the horse leaped into the air.

"Stop! Wait!" cried the Hindu. But the prince shook his head impatiently, and in a few seconds he was sailing away, high up in the air.

"Your Highness," cried the Hindu, "you saw for yourself that the prince did not give me a chance to explain how to manage the horse. He does not know how to turn the horse around and bring him back. I should not be blamed if anything happens to him."

"Miserable creature!" the king cried. "If anything happens to my son, you will surely die! I shall wait three days. If my son does not return by then, I shall cut off your head!"

Thereupon, the Hindu was seized and thrown into prison.

Meanwhile, the young prince was flying through the air on the back of the enchanted horse. "How wonderful this is," he shouted joyfully, as he flew over mountains and rivers. "I can go wherever I please!"

But as night began to fall, he thought of returning. He

pulled the peg this way and that, but the horse kept flying straight ahead. The prince became frightened. "What will happen to me? Oh, how foolish I was not to have listened to the Hindu!"

In the lonely darkness the prince became really terrified. He felt all over the horse, trying to find out if there was some other peg by which he could bring the horse down. Suddenly, he found a little peg behind the horse's ear. He turned it, and sure enough, the horse began to descend. In a few moments it landed on the roof of a large palace.

Not knowing whose palace it was and how he would be received, the prince tiptoed through the hallways, until he came to a large door. Gently, the prince pushed the door open and went in. There, on a magnificent bed, lay a beautiful princess, fast asleep. The prince fell in love with her at once. He knelt down beside her, and taking her soft hand, kissed it gently. This awoke the princess.

At the sight of the handsome prince, she was not frightened, for he was looking at her so lovingly that she knew he meant no harm.

"Who are you?" she asked.

"Most beautiful princess," answered the prince, "I am the son of the King of Persia. This morning I was in my father's palace. Now I find myself in your country, and completely at your mercy. It was by means of a marvelous adventure that I arrived here."

"Gentle prince," answered the princess, "have no fear. You are not among savages. You are in the Kingdom of Bengal. I am the king's daughter, and this is my summer palace. No harm will come to you. I am indeed anxious to hear how you came here."

The prince then told her about the enchanted horse. "My father waits for me at home. I know he must be worried, for I was supposed to return at once. But I love you so dearly that I cannot bear to leave without you. Come with me, to my father, and be my wife!"

When the princess heard these words, she was overjoyed, for she had fallen in love with the prince. Gladly, she agreed to go with him. He led her to the roof top where the horse was waiting. They both mounted the horse, and the prince turned the peg. In a few moments, they were flying through the air, and in two hours' time they arrived in the land of Persia.

The prince landed on the grounds of his own palace, a little distance outside the city. He gave orders to his servants to guard the princess well and to grant her every wish. Then he left to tell his father what had happened, and arrange for the wedding.

The king was overjoyed to see his son alive and well, and happily gave his consent to the marriage. He had the Hindu released from prison and brought before him.

"You are indeed fortunate that my son returned so soon, for in another day you would have been beheaded. Take your horse and go, for I do not ever want to be reminded of these terrible two days when I thought that I had lost my son."

The Hindu was bitterly angry at what the king had done to him, and he felt that he must avenge himself. He heard that the prince had brought back a beautiful princess and that she was waiting in the prince's palace, where the enchanted horse was. He hurried to the prince's palace and spoke to the head steward. "I bring a message from Their Royal Highnesses, the King and Prince. I am to fly the Princess to them, to the city."

The head steward believed him. The princess was happy to go with the Hindu, for she thought that he was going to take her to her beloved. But no sooner had he set her on the horse and mounted beside her, than she realized what had happened, for the Hindu began to laugh and shout, "Ha, ha! There'll be no wedding this day!"

As the horse flew over the city, the prince and his father looked up and saw what was happening. The prince was grief-stricken. He swore that he would never rest until he found his princess again. That very day he put on the clothes of a beggar and set forth to find her.

On and on flew the horse carrying the Hindu and the Princess of Bengal. Toward evening, the Hindu brought the horse down in a far land. He helped the princess to dismount, and was about to go and search for food when a company of horsemen came along. Instantly, the princess jumped to her feet, and running forward, cried, "Help me, noble lords. I am a princess who has

Instantly, the horse leaped into the air.

been kidnaped and carried off by this wicked man!"

Among the noblemen was the King of Cashmere, in whose country they had landed. Upon hearing these words from the beautiful princess, he ordered his men to seize the Hindu and kill him on the spot. The princess was now safe from the Hindu, but she soon saw that she had fallen into another danger. For the King of Cashmere, overcome by her beauty, had no intentions of returning her to her prince. Instead, he gave orders to prepare a feast, for he intended to marry her himself.

When the poor princess heard this, she decided that she would pretend she had gone mad. In this way, she hoped to hold off the king. She deliberately acted wildly and strangely and would let no one come near her. The king sent for his royal doctors. But the princess shrieked and flung herself about so wildly that they could not examine her.

Days went by, and the princess still seemed to be insane. The king sent messengers far and wide to search for skillful doctors who might cure her, but to no avail.

So it happened that the prince, who had been traveling from country to country in search of his loved one, heard the story of the beautiful princess at the King of Cashmere's court, who was mad and could not be cured. He heard, too, that she had arrived there on an enchanted horse.

He hastened to the king's court, and presented himself as a learned doctor. "I can cure the princess," he said, "but only if you do exactly as I say. The first step is that I see her entirely alone."

The king, anxious to do anything to bring about a cure, agreed. So the prince was led to her chamber and was allowed to enter alone. He wept at the sight of his beautiful princess, and cried, "At last I have found you! I have come to rescue you!"

The princess recognized his voice immediately and flung herself into his arms. She told him all that had happened to her. The prince then told her how he had searched far and wide for her, going from country to country. Then he asked her if she knew what the king had done with the enchanted horse.

"I am sure he still has it," said the princess, "but I do not know where."

"Leave everything to me," said the prince. "I have a plan by which we can escape from this land."

So saying, he returned to the king and said, "This is indeed a difficult case. I must know more about it in order to cure the princess. Tell me, how did the princess come to be here in the first place?"

The king then told him how he had found her. "She said that she was brought here on the back of a certain artificial horse which we found nearby, but we have never been able to make the horse fly."

"What you have just told me may be very important," said the prince. "Since she says that she was brought here on this enchanted horse, she might still be under its spell. This spell must be broken. Have the horse brought to the great square in front of your palace tomorrow morning. I feel certain that I will be able to cure the princess."

The king was overjoyed. He had the horse placed in the great square. The princess was led forth and placed upon it. Then the prince had great pans placed around the horse, and had fires kindled in all of them. Into each pan he poured perfumed oil which gave forth thick black clouds of smoke.

When the clouds became so thick that no one could see through them, he ran into the circle and mounted the horse with the princess. He placed his hand on the peg, and just before he turned it to start the horse upward, he shouted in a loud voice, "Foolish King of Cashmere, when you wish to marry a princess, you must first get her consent!"

Then he turned the peg, and the horse carried him and his princess up into the air and out of the reach of the King of Cashmere. Within a few hours, they reached Persia and landed at his father's palace. That very day, they were married, amidst great rejoicing.

Richard the Lion-Hearted

A MINSTREL'S RARE DEVOTION

"YOUR Royal Highness, I would give much to go with you on this glorious journey," said the young minstrel, Blondel. "I know, my faithful Blondel," said King Richard, "and much would I love to have the solace of your company; but I would not risk your sweet voice and lovely music. This perilous war is no place for my gentle minstrel. Stay here in England. I will return, and once more enjoy your devotion and your music."

Thus spoke King Richard the Lion-Hearted, the English King, to his favorite minstrel, Blondel de Nesle. Then Richard set forth on a crusade to the Holy Land. He was leading an army against the Saracens.

The Saracens were the enemies of Christiandom. They held the city of Jerusalem and would permit no Christian to enter it. Christian pilgrims were unable to visit their Holy City.

King Richard had well earned his name of the Lion-Hearted. None of the other kings and nobles who joined in the mighty crusade could compare with him in courage and strength. Sad to say, although they were all fighting as allies, there were many who were jealous of King Richard's fame and hated him.

Many mighty battles were fought, for the Saracens were numerous and strong. King Richard forced Saladin, leader of the Saracens to make a truce. It had been a long and terrible war, and now King Richard was finally able to return home.

Richard set sail, along with many of his brave followers. But one day a terrible storm arose at sea. Richard's ship was smashed to pieces on a rocky shore. Of all who were aboard the vessel, only King Richard survived. Bruised and exhausted, Richard managed to save his life by climbing the rocks of the strange shore. When he had rested, Richard set forth through the strange land. He did not even know the name of the country where he had been cast ashore. He made his way north. He got food where he could. Though he met many people, he was careful not to tell anyone who he was. Richard was well aware that there were many people, even among those who called themselves his allies, who were really his enemies.

Richard had been traveling this way for some time when one day, he found himself in a large town which had a fine castle on a hill. Before Richard could inquire as to who was the lord of the castle, he was seized by a group of the lord's men-at-arms. Richard had been recognized! One of the men-at-arms was an officer in the Duke of Austria's army. He had followed the Duke on his crusade to the Holy Land, and he knew what the great English king looked like.

Now the Duke of Austria was a bitter enemy of King Richard. When Richard was brought before him, the Duke gloated.

"So! the tide has turned," said the Duke of Austria. "You are no longer the proud and powerful leader of great armies. Now you are in my domains and here you shall remain; for no one knows where you are. The world believes you have drowned. The world will keep on thinking so, if I have anything to say." And he ordered King Richard thrust into a dark dungeon.

King Richard was indeed helpless. Here he was, imprisoned in a strange land and no one, except his enemy the Duke and one of the Duke's followers, knew of Richard's plight—or even that he was alive.

A year went by, and the people of England still had no word of their king. The Prince Regent, who had been appointed to rule while King Richard went off to war, was not at all concerned that the true king had not returned. Now *he* would be king. The Prince Regent was only too glad to encourage the belief that Richard the Lion-Hearted was lost.

But there was one man who never lost faith. Blondel, the faithful minstrel, could not believe that his dearly beloved king was dead. Blondel was poor. He had but little money and no followers, yet he set forth alone to find his king. With his harp slung over his shoulder, he traveled on foot throughout Europe, going from castle to castle. He was greeted kindly wherever he went; for in those days, a traveling minstrel was always welcome. There were not many other

. . . came a clear and powerful voice, singing . . .

kinds of entertainment to be had. In this way, Blondel was able to carry on his search for Richard. Wherever the minstrel went, he would ask with guarded questions what prisoners were held in the dungeons beneath the castle.

One day, he came to the castle in which King Richard was held prisoner. Blondel entertained the lords and ladies. Then, as was his custom, he wandered about the castle to talk with the guards. Somehow he learnt that there was an unknown prisoner kept in the largest dungeon.

"He must be someone very important," said the guard, "for he is treated a little better than the others."

Blondel's heart leaped up within him. Could the unknown prisoner be his king? Could he at last have found Richard? That evening, as the sun was setting, Blondel made his way to a spot outside the cell where the unknown prisoner was kept.

Blondel ran his fingers over his harp. Then he began to sing a song which he and King Richard had sung together in the old and happier days.

> *"Long is one night*
> *Long are two nights,*
> *But how can I hold out three?"*

Then he stopped. And then from far down in the depth of the dungeon came a clear and powerful voice, singing the second verse of the song:

"Shorter hath seemed
Many a month
Than this long wait for thee!"

Blondel's heart leaped with joy. It was Richard, his king! Blondel hardly knew what to do. He took up his harp again and this time he sang words of joy and promise to his imprisoned master. He told him in his song how he had searched for him. He told him to rejoice for now help would come. So, by means of song, Blondel was able to communicate with his king without anyone, who might overhear, finding out what was going on between them.

Blondel returned home to England with all speed, bringing the joyful news that King Richard the Lion-Hearted was not dead.

The Prince Regent and his powerful barons were not glad to hear the news and tried to hush it up. But Blondel spread the story about the country and the people of England were overjoyed.

When the people clamored for their king, the Prince Regent announced that the Duke of Austria would not release his royal prisoner until he was paid a tremendous fortune in gold. Though the sum seemed too big to raise, everyone contributed to Richard's ransom. After many months, King Richard, freed at last, came back to England.

Thus, through the great devotion of his faithful minstrel, Blondel, King Richard the Lion-Hearted was returned to his beloved people.

King Arthur

THE MAGIC SWORD THAT CHOSE A KING

MANY, many hundreds of years ago, in the great days of English knighthood, a king named Uther Pendragon ruled over England. It was not a peaceful time. Uther spent many years of his reign defending England against the Saxon invaders.

During these years of war, a son named Arthur was born to the king. To safeguard the young prince from possible harm, Merlin, the court magician, entrusted the infant to a noble and courageous knight, called Sir Ector. Sir Ector and his wife brought up Arthur as their own child, along with their own son, Sir Kay. But they did not know who Arthur really was; and Arthur believed that Sir Ector and his lady were his true parents.

Shortly after he defeated the Saxons, King Uther Pendragon died. Now England was without a king. Great danger prevailed, for there were many powerful lords who aspired to become king, and who would not hesitate to make war upon each other in order to gain the throne. No one but Merlin knew the rightful heir to the throne.

The wise Merlin realized that the jealous nobles would not believe him if he told them about Uther's son, and how the boy had been hidden away shortly after he was born. So Merlin went to the Archbishop of Canterbury and told him to call a meeting of all the most powerful lords and gentlemen-at-arms in the kingdom. They were to come to London at Christmastime. A miracle would show them who was the rightful King of England.

When Christmas came all the nobles of England gathered in the great London church. In front of the church door, there was something that had never been there before. It was a large stone, in the middle of which there was stuck a great sword. On the hilt of the sword, these words were engraved in letters of gold:

I am called Excalibur
Unto a king fair treasure.

Then the Bishop spoke to the assembled nobles. "What say ye, sirs, at this great miracle God has wrought for us! Let us give thanks, for the Lord hath told us who shall be our King. The King shall be he who draws this fair sword from the stone!"

The knights and nobles agreed. First, they all went into the church and offered up prayers of thanksgiving. Then each one in turn tried to pull the sword out of the stone. But not one of them could so much as make it stir.

Seeing this, the Archbishop said, "The man is not here who shall wrest the sword; but never fear, he will come. Let us provide ten worthy knights, men of good fame, to stand guard over the

Arthur took hold of the sword, and . . . drew it out of the stone.

miraculous sword. Mayhap our King will come all alone and unheralded." All was done as the Archbishop ordered.

Soon afterwards, a great tournament of arms was held near London. Knights came from all over the land to joust with each other and try their skill and strength.

Sir Ector's estates lay near London. He and Sir Kay, his son, rode out to take part in the tournament. Along with them rode Arthur, who then was but fifteen years of age.

Early in the tournament, Sir Kay's sword was broken, so he asked young Arthur to ride home and get him another. "That I will, gladly," said Arthur.

But when Arthur returned home he could not find Sir Kay's sword.

Then Arthur, who had passed the church where the nobles had assembled, remembered seeing a sword stuck in a stone there. He did not know the story of the sword. He said to himself, "I will ride to the church and take the sword from the stone. My brother, Sir Kay, shall not be without a sword this day."

When the boy arrived at the church, he dismounted from his horse and went over to the stone. The knights who had been set to guard the stone had gone off to the tournament. Arthur took hold of the sword, and with great ease drew it out of the stone.

Then he rode off to the tournament and gave the sword to Sir Kay. As soon as Sir Kay saw the weapon, he knew it was the miraculous sword. He went to Sir Ector, his father, and said, "Lo!

Here is the miraculous sword! Therefore, I must be King!"

But after Sir Ector had questioned him closely, Sir Kay had to confess that it was Arthur who had brought him the sword.

Sir Ector called Arthur to him. "How came you by this sword?" he asked. Arthur told him how he had gotten it. To make certain, Sir Ector brought Arthur back to the church and had him place the sword back into the stone.

"Now show me how you drew the sword," Sir Ector said. Again Arthur drew the sword out of the stone. Sir Ector fell on his knees before Arthur, and Sir Kay did likewise.

"Alas, dear father and brother," said Arthur. "Why do you kneel before me?"

"Nay, my lord Arthur," answered Sir Ector, "I was never your true father. You are of royal blood." Then Sir Ector told Arthur how he had been brought to him as a baby by Merlin the magician.

Then together they went to the Archbishop and Sir Ector told how Arthur had wrested the magical sword. By command of the Archbishop, all the lords and barons and gentlemen-at-arms were once again gathered in the courtyard. Arthur replaced the sword in the stone. Each one in turn tried once more to move it, but none could do so, save Arthur.

Whereupon they knelt down; and each, one and all, proclaimed Arthur his King. After that, Arthur was crowned; and there he swore to be a good King and to govern England with true justice all the days of his life.

Canute the Wise

THE KING WHO SHAMED HIS COURTIERS

IN olden days, there ruled over England a wise and venerable king named Canute. Like most people who are in positions of great power, Canute was surrounded by courtiers who flattered him constantly. They all vied to gain his favor by telling the king how great and wise and powerful he was.

"O, great king," said one, "there is no one so mighty as you."

"Your Majesty," said another, "everything you do is wise and great!"

King Canute had to listen to all this praise constantly. Many foolish men in his position would have become puffed up with pride and conceit. Not so King Canute. He was far too wise a man to have his head turned by silly flattery.

One day when the king and his court were assembled in the great hall, one of the most persistent of the king's flatterers bowed low and said, "Oh, who is like unto you, great king? None is so powerful. The world kneels before you!"

King Canute rose up. "Let us go down to the sea," he said.

"Stop, oh sea! I command you to come no further!"

His servants carried his great chair down to the nearby sea-shore, while all the court wondered at his action. When everyone had reached the shore, the king turned to his court and said, "Am I really the greatest king in the world?"

"Oh yes!" they answered, with one voice.

"And does everything obey me?" he asked.

"Why, yes," they said, "who would dare to disobey you?"

"Then, of course, the sea obeys me, does it not?" said the king.

His courtiers stood silent for a moment. They were afraid to say anything except yes; so they replied, "It is true, great king. Everything obeys you."

Then King Canute stood up and said, "Stop, oh sea! I command you to come no further!"

But the waves rolled in just the same. As the tide rose, the waves came farther and farther up the shore until they splashed over the feet of the powerful king and even wet his royal garments.

King Canute then took off his crown and threw it into the waves.

"Look, ye vain and foolish men!" he cried, "How weak and powerless we are. My kingdom and my power are as nothing before the great King, the King of Kings, who rules the world. It is He you should praise and glorify, not any mortal man!"

And King Canute strode away, leaving his courtiers standing foolish and abashed by his rebuke. They would not soon forget the lesson the wise king had taught them.

Robert Bruce and the Spider

HOW A KING LEARNED COURAGE FROM AN INSECT

ROBERT BRUCE was a much troubled King of Scotland. The English were at war with him, and his country was in great danger.

The English seemed to be much stronger. Again and again they drove the Scotsmen back. Things became so bad that finally Bruce, the King himself, had to flee to the mountains to save his life.

The wretched King hid in a little hut. He was tired and cold and hungry. He lay in a corner of the cabin, depressed and in despair. "I might as well give up," he thought. "My men are scattered. Six times we have been thrown back. How many times can we gather our forces to fight? How will we ever succeed in driving the English from our land?"

Just then he happened to notice a spider crawling along one of the rafters. The spider spun a long thread. Then the spider swung himself on the end of the thread trying to reach across to another rafter to attach the thread and start his web. But the thread broke and the spider fell to the floor.

"O, little spider, you have taught me a great lesson."

Robert Bruce watched. The spider again began his long and difficult task. Once again he climbed the wall and spun his thread. But once again he failed to reach the beam and he fell to the ground. Bruce was so interested in the spider that he forgot his own troubles. Six times the spider tried to reach the rafter — six times he failed. *The seventh time the thread held!*

"Bravo!" cried Robert Bruce. "O, little spider, you have taught me a great lesson. No matter how hard and difficult a task may be, if you try and try again, you will win through! I, like you, have had six failures. Perhaps my seventh attempt, like yours, will be successful."

Alfred and the Cakes

A KING'S JUSTICE AND MERCY

IN England, many hundreds of years ago, there ruled a king who is still known today, as he was in his own time, as Alfred the Great.

During Alfred's reign, England was invaded by the fierce and warlike Vikings. If all Alfred had ever done was drive out the Vikings, as he did, that would have been enough to make his name famous. But he has always been remembered as well for his goodness and justice.

Here is a story which has come down to us all the way from that early time, showing how kind and how fair-minded Alfred was.

At one point during its battles with the Vikings, Alfred's small army was taken by surprise and scattered, and Alfred himself was forced to flee for his life.

Disguised as a shepherd, the king wandered through the woods and swamps for several days until, finally, he chanced upon a poor woodcutter's hut.

Weary and hungry, he knocked on the door. The woodcutter's

wife answered. Courteously, Alfred asked if she could spare him something to eat and a place to sleep in the little hut.

The woman looked at the ragged stranger in pity, not knowing who he was. "Come in," she said. "Our hut is poor, but what we have, we will share. You can earn your supper by watching these cakes I am baking, while I go out and milk the cow. Watch them carefully. Be sure to take the cakes off the fire before they burn."

Alfred thanked her and sat down before the fire.

A moment later all his cares came to his mind. How was he going to rally his army? Where was the best place to attack the Vikings? What was the best way to defeat them and drive them from England? Deep in his problems, Alfred forgot all about the cakes.

In a little while, the woodcutter's wife returned to the hut. She found it filled with smoke. The cakes on the hearth were burnt to a crisp. But Alfred still sat before the fire, deep in thought. He had not even noticed that the cakes were burning! The poor woman fairly exploded with anger.

"You lazy, daydreaming knave!" she cried. "Look what you've done! Now there'll be no supper for any of us!" And she gave him an unmerciful tongue-lashing. Alfred hung his head in shame and did not say a word.

In the middle of this scolding, the woodcutter came home. He recognized the stranger at once. "Hush, woman!" he cried. "Know you not who honors our home? It is our great and noble lord, King Alfred himself!"

"You lazy, daydreaming knave! Look what you've done!"

The poor woman was terrified. She fell to her knees and began to babble apologies, begging him not to have her killed or punished for speaking to him so disrespectfully.

But the noble Alfred bade her rise. "You were entirely right in scolding me," he told her. "Anybody who accepts a task, be he king or peasant, accepts the duty of seeing that it is well performed. I agreed to watch the cakes; I let them burn. I well deserve your harsh words."

Thus, with honesty and forgiveness, Alfred repaid the woman's kindness to a poor stranger. Soon he gathered his army again and drove the Vikings out of England.

The Inchcape Rock

A PIRATE'S PUNISHMENT

FAR up in the wild North Sea, there was once a spot most dreaded by sailors. It had spelled doom and disaster to many an unfortunate ship. An enormous jagged rock rose up there from the ocean's floor—a rock utterly hidden from sight, for the top of it rose to just a few feet below the level of the water. One had to be a clever mariner, indeed, to pass through that terrible sea without smashing the ship against the murderous points of the Inchcape Rock. During a storm it was quite impossible to figure out just where the dreaded rock lay, and it was then that the cries of the victims of shipwreck would fill the air.

One day, over a hundred years ago, a kind old abbot set forth from the shore nearby. In his boat, he carried a buoy and bell.

"We will attach the bell to the buoy, and then attach the buoy to the Inchcape Rock. In this way, the movement of the waves will cause the bell to sway and to ring. When mariners hear the ringing of the bell, they will know that they are near the terrible Inchcape Rock, and they will steer their ships away from the sound."

. . . the sea came pouring in through tremendous holes in its side.

But one calm and sunny day, the pirate, Ralph the Rover, was sailing by. His ship was crammed with loot which he had stolen from honest merchantmen. He had killed many innocent people and had sunk many unarmed ships to gain this wealth.

When he heard the ringing of the abbot's bell, he said to his men, "I've got an idea! We'll let down a small boat and row over to the buoy. Then we'll disconnect the bell and sink it to the bottom of the sea!"

The fact that innocent people might die because of his deed only gave more pleasure to that evil man.

He had not gone very far away—just a day's sail—when a terrible storm arose. Ralph the Rover and his men were blown far off their course. For two days, the storm raged. The pirates didn't know where they were. Suddenly, a terrible crash shook the ship! The next moment the sea came pouring in through tremendous holes in its side.

"It's the Inchcape Rock! We are lost!" cried the pirate. And indeed they were! Every last one of that bloodthirsty crew was drowned. The fate they had so cruelly planned for others had overtaken them. *"Dig not a pit for others, lest you fall therein."*

The Bell of Atri

HOW JUSTICE WAS WON

HIGH in the mountains of Italy, there was a little town called Atri, which was ruled by a just and kindly king. Once, long ago, the people of Atri watched with great curiosity while a marble bell tower was erected in the center of the market place. All they could learn about the tower was that it was being built on the orders of the king. At length, it was finished, and a large and beautiful bell was hung in the belfry. Then the king's messenger called the towns-people together.

When they were all assembled in the market place, the king stepped before the tower and spoke. "My people," he said, "this bell which I am giving you has been cast by the finest craftsmen; it is one of the best bells in all Italy. And yet,"—here the king paused— "and yet, I hope that the bell will not often be rung."

A buzz went up through the crowd. Since the king was giving the town a fine bell, why should he not want it rung? The answer was not long in coming.

"When this bell is heard," continued the king, "it shall mean only one thing. It shall mean that someone has been wronged! We shall call it the Bell of Justice. It must never be rung except by someone who has been wronged and wants justice done. When the sound of the bell is heard, the judges of Atri will immediately assemble in the market place to set right whatever wrong has been done. All who seek justice shall have the right to use this bell, be they rich or poor, old or young. See, I have had a long rope attached to the bell—a rope that reaches almost to the ground—so that even a child may be able to reach it."

The people of Atri were grateful to the king for the goodness and wisdom of his gift. The Bell of Justice became just what the king had wanted it to be. When the bell was not heard for long periods, the people were glad, because it meant that no one had been wronged. And when the bell was rung, they were glad too, because they knew justice would be done, and the wrong would be set right.

After many years of service, the tower and bell, of marble and bronze, were as fine and beautiful as ever. But the bell rope, frayed and worn by age and weather, finally broke off. Only a short length remained. Seeing this, the judges said, "We must replace the rope. Remember what our good king said? It must be long enough for even a child to reach."

But in the town there was no rope long enough or strong enough for the purpose. So the judges sent a messenger to a large city, several days' journey away, to buy a new rope for the bell. In the meantime, one of the townspeople cut a long vine and tied it to the short rope, so that their beloved bell would not be out of service, even for a short time.

The messenger, hurrying through the outskirts of Atri on his way to the large city, passed the house of a miserly old man, who lived on a farm with only an aged and scrawny horse as a companion. In his younger days, the old miser had been a knight, and his horse had served him faithfully in many a gallant fight. But now the knight had turned into a greedy, miserly man, who hated to part with so much as a penny of his considerable fortune. He even grudged his faithful old horse the bit of fodder necessary to feed him.

On the very day the messenger had hurried past his house, the old man had said to himself, "Of what earthly use is this old horse to me? He can no longer work. I cannot even sell him, for no one would buy an old, sick horse. Every day he costs me money to feed him. I shall put a stop to it!"

So he turned the horse out of his stable and drove him away from his land. Now the poor animal would have to search for his own food.

Where could the old horse go? For two days and nights the wretched horse wandered through the countryside, nibbling a little grass where he could find it. Lame and sick, shivering through the cold nights, he walked the lonely roads. Finally, he made his way into the town of Atri. As he limped into the market place, the famished animal caught sight of the green vine hanging from the bell rope. Since it had just been placed there, its leaves were still fresh. Hungrily, the horse stretched forth his thin neck toward the vine.

Suddenly, the people of Atri heard their Bell of Justice ringing. Through the town the loud, clear pealing of the bell echoed and seemed to say:

> *"Someone has done me wrong!*
> *Someone has done me wrong!*
> *Come and hear my case!*
> *Come and hear my case!*
> *For I have been wronged!"*

Quickly, the judges put on their robes and hurried to the market place, followed by many of the townspeople. But when they reached the bell tower, all they saw was an old horse nibbling at the vine.

"What is this?" asked the judges.

One of the townspeople spoke up. "It is the miser's horse," he said. "See, he has come for justice. For who does not know that he has been shamefully treated by his master."

Then the people of the town added their voices to his. "Yes," they said, "for long years this horse served his master well. Now he has been turned out to die of cold and hunger, while his master sits counting his gold. He pleads his case in the only way he can. Let him have justice!"

"He shall have justice," answered the judges. "Go bring the

. . . all they saw was an old horse nibbling at the vine.

miser to the market place."

The old miser was brought before the judges.

"Shame upon you," they said. "Is this how you repay your faithful servant? Now we command you to take half your gold and set it aside for your horse. He shall have a warm stall with plenty of fodder and a green field to graze in during the day."

The miser was forced to do as he was ordered. And so it was that the Bell of Atri brought justice even to one of the most helpless and forsaken of creatures.

Till Eulenspiegel

BRUNSWICK'S GREAT PRANKSTER

TO Till Eulenspiegel, life was always one huge joke — and the joke was usually on somebody else!

There was the time for example, when Till went to the fair riding a magnificent horse. There he met a crafty horse dealer who had cheated many a poor peasant. The dealer tried to get Till to part with his horse for a ridiculously low price. Till refused to be trapped.

Finally Till turned to the dealer and said, "I will make no secret of my feelings. I don't like you. In fact, I dislike you so much that I will offer you this proposal: I will give you my horse for no money at all — on one condition. You put your arms around yonder barrel while I give you three hard whacks with this wide belt from my coat. Then I will turn the horse over to you, free and clear."

At first, the dealer was furious. But as he looked at the fine horse, his greed got the better of him; and he accepted Till's terms.

The horse dealer stretched his arms around the barrel. Till picked up the belt, lifted it over his head, and let go with a resounding wallop. "Oh!" groaned the horse dealer. "This is terrible! But go ahead. There are only two more to go!"

Again Till lifted up the belt, and laid it smartly across the horse dealer's back.

"Ouch!" yelled the dealer. "Hurry up and give me the third stroke. Let's get this thing over with!"

But Till replaced the belt in his coat. "That's all for now," he said. "According to our agreement you don't get the horse until I've given you three whacks. And I'm in no hurry to give you the third whack — no hurry at all!" Then he mounted his horse and rode away, leaving the horse trader spluttering with rage, and the towns-people chuckling with glee.

One cold winter night, Till Eulenspiegel, numb with cold, entered the village inn. One look around the room showed him that all the nice warm seats near the fire were taken. For a moment Till said nothing. Then, in a loud whisper — loud enough for everyone to hear — he said to the innkeeper, "Do you think it will snow any more tonight? I hope not, because I dropped my purse just outside, and I'd like a night's rest before I go out to search for it. But if it continues to snow, I'll have to go right out now before my purse is completely covered."

A crafty look came into the innkeeper's eyes. "Oh, no," he said, "I'm sure it won't snow any more tonight."

In a few minutes, the innkeeper made some excuse about looking after the horses and left the room. And Till was not at all surprised when shortly afterward, the men who were sitting by the fire got up, one by one, and sauntered out into the cold night.

Soon Till had his choice of the most comfortable chairs. He chuckled as he settled down for a good night's sleep next to the fire. For of course his purse was safe and sound in his coat pocket all the time!

Till once accepted the position of court jester to the Count of Limburg. One day Till said to the count, "It may interest your excellency to know that there is nothing about you I don't know. For instance, I even know that you have a horseshoe-shaped birthmark on your shoulder blade."

"I certainly do not have such a mark," answered the count.

"Ah, but you do," insisted Till. "In fact, I am so sure of it that I am willing to wager you ten gold crowns."

"Do you really want to bet?" asked the count. "Well, all right, if you insist." And the count rubbed his hands in glee, for he knew that all he had to do was take off his clothes to prove to Till that he had no such mark on his shoulder blade. So he quickly undressed and turned his back for Till to see.

"I have lost," Till admitted. "You are right, my lord, but I don't understand it. Why should your valet tell me in confidence that you had such a mark on your back? Wait till I see that fellow!"

The count was pleased as punch. It was a rare treat to put anything over on Till. "Oh, don't take it too hard," he said, and threw Till a purse. "Here, Till, console yourself with this money."

That evening, as the count was making ready for bed, he asked his valet, "Whatever made you tell Till that I have a birthmark on my shoulder blade? I ought to dismiss you for gossiping falsely about me. But I did so much enjoy winning that bet against Till that I will forgive you."

The valet was astounded. "But my lord," he said, "I never said anything at all to Till about you. I don't know what you mean!"

The count then told his valet about the wager. "Oh ho!" he laughed, "you should have seen Till's face when I took off my clothes and showed him he was wrong!"

Then the valet let out an anguished groan. "Oh that rascal Till! That villain! Yesterday he came to me and boasted that he would have the clothes off your back. The impudent fellow, to talk like that! When I protested, he offered to wager me twenty pieces of gold. Why, I would have bet everything I own against it. Now Till wins twenty pieces of gold from me, whereas he lost only ten pieces of gold to you. He's still ten pieces to the good."

When the count saw Till the next morning, he said, "I must admit you fooled me, but some day I shall really get the best of you."

"Well," said Till, "now is as good as any time. Here is something I am sure you cannot do; you cannot repeat seven words after me exactly as I say them, without making a mistake."

"Why you must take me for a fool," said the count. "A simple thing like that! I'll bet you fifty pieces of gold that I shall repeat your words exactly, whatever they might be."

"All right," said Till, "let's begin. Say after me: *I give you,*"

" ...I'm in no hurry to give you the third whack ...!"

"I give you," repeated the count.

"My velvet cloak," continued Till.

"My velvet cloak," said the count frowning, for he saw that this was going to cost him something.

"Wrong!" exclaimed Till.

"What do you mean, wrong?" cried the count. "I repeated every word you said."

"Not every word," said Till, "but I will give you another chance."

Till started again, *"I am,"*

"I am," said the count.

"A foolish old man," said Till.

The count grew red in the face, but he continued, "A foolish old man."

"Wrong!" cried Till.

"No, it isn't wrong!" shouted the count. "I repeated every word exactly, even though I think you are a rascal to make me say such things. Why you even made me give you my cloak. Yet now you say I am wrong. I believe you just won't admit that you lost the bet."

"Not at all," said Till. "It is you who have lost, even though I gave you two chances. You repeated six words after me correctly, but the seventh word, the word *wrong,* you did not repeat. If you had repeated that word correctly, you would not only have won, but you would have undone all the foolishness that went before."

The count burst into laughter! How could he ever hope to win against a fellow like that? He paid his forfeit and actually thanked Till for amusing him.

Soon after, Till left the Count's court at Limburg and traveled to the town of Magdeburg. Here he proclaimed himself to be a doctor. Of course, he didn't know the first thing about the art of healing. But Till dressed himself in a long gown and a wig, such as the doctors used to wear at that time, and set up an office. People soon came to consult him. He dosed his patients with nothing but sugar pills. Since most of them got better anyway, and since Till's manner was always so dignified and confident, he soon enjoyed an excellent reputation as a doctor. One day, the chief of the town's charity hospital came to him and said, "I have so many patients in my hospital that I cannot begin to attend to them all. Can you help me take care of some of them?"

Till answered, "If I should cure all your patients in a single day so that there is no one left in your hospital, will you give me a hundred pieces of gold?"

"Why," said the chief, "if you could do such a thing I would gladly pay you such a sum."

"Well, then, it is settled," said Till. "Now let us go and examine your patients. I have to work fast you know."

They went over to the hospital together. Till walked from bed to bed. At each bed, he whispered into the ear of the man lying there. "Listen carefully," he told each of them, "this is important, and it is just between you and me. I can cure you but only in a very difficult way. I have to take one person from amongst the people in this hospital and burn him to a powder. Out of that powder, I will make a medicine and give it to the rest of you to drink. Then you will be completely well again. There is no other way. If you want me to do this, I shall select the person amongst you who is the most sick and who is not likely to live much longer anyhow. Out of him, I will make the magic medicine."

Each of the patients, anxious to be well, agreed to this proposition, adding that he himself was not so very ill — but that the man in the *next* bed certainly was.

The next morning Till told the chief doctor that everyone in the hospital was cured as he had promised. "Come with me to the hospital now and I shall prove it to you," said Till. Till stood at the door of the hospital ward and called out, "All those who are perfectly well get up and leave. Only those who are sick remain."

Now every one of the patients thought that if he stayed behind he might be chosen as the one who was the sickest. One and all, each hurried out as fast as his legs could carry him. The delighted hospital chief gave Till the hundred pieces of gold and thanked him profusely. Needless to say, Till left the town of Magdeburg without further delay. He thought it better not to be around when the sick men returned to the hospital.

Though it is hundreds of years since that merry madcap played his pranks, the name of Till Eulenspiegel still brings a smile to the people of Brunswick.

The Pied Piper of Hamelin

A MINSTREL'S ENCHANTED MUSIC

HAMELIN Town was in terrible trouble! Once it had been thriving and happy, but now alas! now it was being ruined by a most extraordinary plague. Rats! Thousands of them! Millions of them! Rats! Rats! Rats! Their number was endless! And rats of all kinds and shapes!

As Robert Browning, the poet, put it:

> *They fought the dogs, and killed the cats;*
> > *And bit the babies in the cradles;*
> *And ate the cheeses out of the vats;*
> > *And licked the soup from the cooks' own ladles;*
> *Split open the kegs of salted sprats;*
> *Made nests inside men's Sunday hats;*
> *And even spoiled the women's chats*
> > *By drowning their speaking*
> > *With shrieking and squeaking*
> *In fifty different sharps and flats!*

Nothing — absolutely nothing — seemed to help! The people of Hamelin appealed to the Mayor and the burghers of the town Corporation to do something. *Anything!* The unhappy officials could only assure the townspeople that they were giving the matter deep thought. Then they would hide in the council chamber, and sit and stare dumbly at each other. No one could think of what to do!

One day while the Mayor and the Corporation were meeting in the council hall they heard a knocking on the door. "Come in!" the Mayor said. And in did come the strangest figure!

> *His queer long coat from heel to head*
> *Was half of yellow and half of red;*
> *And he himself was tall and thin,*
> *With sharp blue eyes, each like a pin;*
> *And light loose hair, yet swarthy skin,*
> *But lips where smiles went out and in.*

The Mayor and the Corporation looked at each other in astonishment. "Here now!" cried the Mayor, when he found his voice. "We have grave deliberations and serious work to do! State your business, clown, and be quick about it!" The stranger looked up shyly.

> *He advanced to the council table:*
> *And, "Please your honours," said he, "I'm able*

By means of a secret charm to draw
All creatures living beneath the sun
That creep or swim or fly or run,
After me so, as you never saw!
And I chiefly use my charm
On creatures that do people harm:
The mole and toad and newt and viper.
And people call me the Pied Piper."

The odd-looking fellow hesitated a moment, looked at the thunderstruck officials, and then went on:

"If I can rid your town of rats
Will you give me a thousand guilders?"
"One? Fifty thousand!" was the exclamation
Of the astonished Mayor and Corporation.

"Then, good sirs," said the Piper. "Now that we are agreed on the terms, I think you will also agree that the sooner it were done, the better." He bowed low and stepped into the street.

With an odd smile playing about his face, the Pied Piper lifted his pipe to his lips and began to play. No sooner had his first shrill notes echoed through the square when a muttering sound was heard. Then the muttering grew to a grumbling, and the grumbling grew to a mighty rumbling. And out of the houses, from every alley, street

Out came the children running.

and square the rats came tumbling!

> *Great rats, small rats, lean rats, brawny rats,*
> *Brown rats, black rats, grey rats, tawny rats,*
> *Grave old plodders, gay young friskers,*
>   *Fathers, mothers, uncles, cousins,*
> *Cocking tails and pricking whiskers,*
>   *Families by tens and dozens;*
> *Brothers, sisters, husbands, wives —*
>   *Followed the Piper for their lives.*

And do you know where the Piper went? Straight to the banks of the Weser River. The Piper waded in. The rats, as if entranced, followed him — followed the Pied Piper into the stream — followed the Pied Piper and drowned!

Every one in the town was simply overjoyed at being rid of the loathsome rats. As you might expect, Hamelin celebrated loud and long. Yes, the rats were gone; but the Mayor waited to be sure they were gone for good.

> *"Go," cried the Mayor, "and get long poles!*
> *Poke out the nests and block up the holes!*
> *Consult with carpenters and builders,*
> *And leave in our town not even a trace*
> *Of the rats!" — when suddenly, up the face*

> *Of the Piper perked, in the market place,*
> *With a, "First, if you please my thousand guilders!"*

A thousand guilders! The Mayor's jaw dropped in consternation. Oh, of course, there had been some mention of payment — but a thousand guilders! Why, that sum would go a long way toward buying the Mayor and Corporation new robes — not to mention filling their cellars with fine wines. Pay this beggar *a thousand guilders*! O heavens! What an idea!

> *"Besides," quoth the Mayor with a knowing wink,*
> *"Our business was done at the river's brink;*
> *We saw with our eyes the vermin sink,*
> *And what's dead can't come to life, I think.*
> *So, friend, we're not the folks to shrink*
> *From the duty of giving you something for drink,*
> *And a matter of money to put in your poke*
> *But as for the guilders, what we spoke*
> *Of them, as you very well know, was in joke.*
> *Besides, our losses have made us thrifty.*
> *A thousand guilders! Come, take fifty!"*

The Piper's smiling face clouded with anger: "Pay me my thousand guilders!" he cried, "or you shall find me piping in another fashion!"

But the Mayor was scornful. What could a queer-looking stranger like the Piper do, one against the whole city of Hamelin?

"You threaten us fellow? Do your worst,
Blow your pipe there till you burst!"

"So be it!" said the Piper. He bowed mockingly to the Mayor and the Councillors, and lifted his pipe to his lips. Before he had blown three notes —

There was a rustling, that seemed like a bustling
Of merry crowds jostling at pitching and hustling;
Small feet were pattering, wooden shoes clattering,
Little hands clapping and little tongues chattering,
And, like fowls in a farm-yard when barley is scattering,
Out came the children running.
All the little boys and girls,
With rosy cheeks and flaxen curls,
And sparkling eyes and teeth like pearls,
Tripping and skipping, ran merrily after
The wonderful music with shouting and laughter.
The Mayor was dumb; and the Council stood
As if they were changed into blocks of wood,
Unable to move a step, or cry
To the children merrily skipping by —

And could only follow with the eye
That joyous crowd at the Piper's back.

Out of the town marched the Piper, and out of the town marched the children of Hamelin, dancing at his heels. The Mayor and the townsfolk were spellbound. They seemed to have been deprived of the power of movement and speech by the Piper's music. When the Piper came to the river Weser, he crossed the bridge and led the children toward a high mountain that lay beyond.

"Ah, that will stop him!" cried the people of the town. "That mountain is much too steep for anyone to climb!" They strained their eyes to watch as the children approached the mountain. But the people of Hamelin were due for a great shock. The Piper kept right on going, and the children followed his music — followed right to the base of the mountain —

When, lo, as they reached the mountain's side,
A wondrous portal opened wide,
As if a cavern was suddenly hollowed;
And the Piper advanced and the children followed
And when all were in to the very last,
The door in the mountain-side shut fast.

An anguished cry rose throughout Hamelin Town as the towns-folk saw the mountain door close. Now all their children had disappeared forever!

All? No! The townspeople glimpsed a solitary figure limping back toward the town. They rushed out to meet a little lame boy. He was crying bitterly because he had not been able to run fast enough to keep up with the Piper and his playmates; so he had been left behind when the mountain closed.

"Tell us!" cried the townspeople. "Tell us why — what made the children follow the Piper?" And the little lame boy explained:

> " . . . he led us," he said, "to a joyous land,
> Joining the town; and just at hand,
> Where waters gushed and fruit trees grew,
> And flowers put forth a fairer hue,
> And everything was strange and new.
> The sparrows were brighter than peacocks here;
> And the dogs outran our fallow deer;
> And honey-bees had lost their stings;
> And horses were born with eagle's wings!"

Yes, such was the magic of the Piper's music. So the people of Hamelin lived in sorrow the rest of their days — days that no longer held the sound of children's laughter. They had learned their lesson and received their just due. They had learned that a promise made is a promise to be kept.

Rip Van Winkle

THE STRANGE LITTLE MEN OF THE MOUNTAIN

ONCE upon a time, in a little Catskill mountain village close by the majestic Hudson River, there lived a pleasant, good-natured fellow by the name of Rip Van Winkle.

Everybody was very fond of Rip for he was always ready to lend a helping hand to his neighbor. But his wife was always in a temper with him, for she could never get him to work for himself. So she kept scolding him and telling him what a worthless fellow he was.

Rip's only escape was to flee with his dog, Wolf, up into the mountains, and go hunting, away from the sound of his wife's nagging voice.

One day after Dame Van Winkle had scolded him even more violently than usual, Rip picked up his gun, whistled to his dog, and fled. There was plenty of small game to be found in the mountains and the day went by almost before he knew it.

Late in the afternoon, Rip threw himself down to rest on a little hillock. It was just beginning to get dark. Rip knew that he ought to be on his way home. But the thought of Dame Van Winkle's sharp tongue made him hate to go. Just then he heard a voice calling from a distance. "Rip Van Winkle! Rip Van Winkle!" Rip looked round but could see nothing.

Again, as if from a distance, came the cry, "Rip Van Winkle! Rip Van Winkle!" At the sound, Rip's dog, Wolf, gave a low growl. The hair bristled on Wolf's back and he sulked closer to his master's side.

A feeling of fear crept over Rip. He stared hard in the direction from which the call had come. Then he saw a strange-looking figure climbing up the mountainside. In the fading light, Rip saw what looked like a very short man, struggling up the hill, carrying a heavy load on his back. As he drew near, Rip was amazed at the appearance of the stranger. He was as short as a boy, but he had a long grey beard, and a serious-looking old face. Without a word, the newcomer motioned to Rip to help him with a large keg which he carried on his shoulder. Rip stepped forward and, in his usual friendly fashion, shared the burden. The little old man led the way upwards, towards a deep gully between two mountain peaks.

As the two of them walked without speaking, Rip heard rumbling sounds, like distant peals of thunder. Rip would have liked to move faster in order to escape the coming storm; he would also have liked to chat with the old man and find out why he was carrying a keg of ale up into the wild mountains. But the strange and serious manner of his new companion did not seem to invite conversation.

Suddenly the narrow path opened out into a green meadow between two high cliffs and a strange sight met his eyes.

Clustered at one end of the field was a whole company of little men, dressed in costumes the like of which Rip had never seen. They were all busily engaged in playing ninepins on the green. But the oddest thing about them, aside from their quaint dress, was their serious manner as they played. The odd little men went about their game with grave faces, no one smiling, no one talking or laughing. And as the ball knocked down the ninepins, Rip heard the rolling, pealing sound that he had mistaken for thunder a little while before.

As Rip and his companion approached, the bowlers stopped their game and stared at Rip in silence. At a signal from the little man he had accompanied up the mountain, Rip lowered the keg to the ground. Then Rip's companion started pouring the contents of the keg into huge copper pitchers. He motioned to Rip to serve the company with ale from the pitchers.

Rip obeyed. Gravely, without a word being spoken, the little men drank the ale. Then they returned to their silent game of ninepins, paying no attention at all to Rip.

Little by little Rip began to lose his fear, and, since no one seemed to be looking at him, he decided that he might as well help himself to a drink of ale. One drink served only to make him thirsty for another, and then another, and another. Before he knew it, Rip had drunk so much that his head began to whirl dizzily, and he found it difficult to keep his eyes open. Soon Rip was fast asleep.

When he awoke, Rip found himself back on the little green hillock where he had first heard his name called. It was morning — a bright and beautiful, sunshiny morning.

"Great heavens," thought Rip, "I have slept here on the mountain all night!"

Then Rip remembered the strange happenings of the night before — the queer traveler with the keg of ale, the sad-looking little men at their game of ninepins, the ale which he had drunk.

"Oh, those drinks I took!" thought Rip. "How on earth will I excuse myself to Dame Van Winkle for staying away all night?" As he sat up he noticed his joints were stiff.

Rip looked around for his gun, but in place of his own shiny, well-oiled musket, he found a rusted old firelock. He looked around for his dog, but Wolf was nowhere to be seen. Rip whistled for him, he shouted Wolf's name, but no dog came trotting to him.

He decided to go back to the place where he had been the night before. If any of the men were there, he would demand that they give him back his dog and his gun.

Rip got to his feet and made his way back along the trail. But when he got to the meadow where he had spent the previous evening, Rip was astonished to see the glen filled by a rushing mountain stream. He clambered up the hillside and looked about him again. This was the spot all right, but how could the green meadow have filled up with a roaring mountain torrent overnight?

Rip shook his head in wonder. Once more he whistled for his

dog, but again, there was no answer. Full of sadness at the loss of his dog, Rip turned homeward.

As he approached his village, Rip met a number of men and women, but not one face was familiar. This surprised him, for Rip thought he surely knew everyone in town. The clothes of the passers-by, too, seemed to be of a different fashion than he had ever seen before. Strangely enough, these men and women stared back at Rip, their mouths agape in surprise, as if *he* were a queer-looking stranger. A group of boys and girls stopped their play and ran after him, laughing and stroking their chins. Self-consciously, Rip fingered his own chin. He was astounded to find that he had a long beard! And when he came into the village Rip was more puzzled than ever, for even the village looked different. There were strange houses; strange names over the shop doors, and strange people in the streets.

"Oh, that ale I drank last night!" he thought. "It must have addled my poor head."

Rip made his way to his own house in fear and trembling, expecting every minute to hear the shrill voice of Dame Van Winkle. And there poor Rip Van Winkle had his greatest shock of all. He found his house gone to decay — the roof fallen in, the windows broken, the door off its hinges.

Rip called loudly for his wife and children — but his own voice echoed back to him and all was silence again.

Now he hurried to the village inn, to look for his friends with whom he had passed so many hours at play and talk. But the inn,

. . . boys and girls stopped their play and ran after him.

too, was utterly changed. The building was painted an entirely different color than he had remembered; the sign above it no longer read "King George's Tavern"; but instead, over the door was a sign saying: "Union Hotel".

As Rip walked down the street in his queer shabby clothes, with his long grizzly beard and his rusty old gun, a small army of women and children tagged along at his heels. He walked over to a group of men who were standing nearby. In a trembling voice he asked for his friends. "Where is Nicholas Vedder?" he asked.

For a moment, no one spoke. Then an old man in a thin piping voice stepped out from the crowd and said, "Nicholas Vedder! Why he's been dead these last 18 years."

Rip's head whirled. "Where is Brom Dutcher?" he asked.

"Oh, he went off to the army in the beginning of the war and he's never come back."

Upon hearing these words Rip's heart died within him. Every answer puzzled him. He had no courage to ask after any more friends, but cried out in despair, "Does anybody here know Rip Van Winkle?"

"Oh, Rip Van Winkle!" exclaimed two or three people at once. "We know *him* all right. There he is leaning against that tree."

Rip looked and saw a young man who seemed like a twin of himself, when he had gone up the mountain. Poor Rip was completely dumbfounded. He took off his hat and sank down on a bench. One of the men demanded, "Who are you? What is your name?"

"God knows!" exclaimed Rip. "I am not myself — I am some-body else — that's me over there — no, that's somebody else got into my shoes. I was myself last night, but I fell asleep on the mountain and they changed my gun; and everything is changed, and I can't tell what's my name and who I am."

Just then a pretty young woman passed through the crowd. She had a plump little baby in her arms who began to cry at the sight of Rip. The young woman comforted the baby and said, "Hush, Rip, hush, the old man won't hurt you." Then Rip looked up and stared at the young woman.

"What is your name, my good woman?" he asked.

"Judith Gardiner."

"And your father's name?"

"Ah, poor man!" she said. "Rip Van Winkle was his name, but it's twenty years since he went away from home with his gun and has never been heard of since — his dog came home without him; but whether he shot himself or was carried away by Indians nobody knows. I was but a little girl then."

"And your mother," asked Rip, "where is she?"

"She is dead, too, God rest her soul, these ten years."

Then Rip caught his daughter and her child in his arms. "I am your father!" cried he — "Young Rip Van Winkle once. Old Rip Van Winkle now. Doesn't anybody know poor Rip Van Winkle?"

As everyone stood amazed, an old woman tottered out from the crowd and looking into Rip's face for a moment, exclaimed,

"Sure enough, it is Rip Van Winkle. It is Rip himself. Welcome home, old neighbor. Where have you been these twenty long years?"

It did not take long for Rip to tell his story, for the whole twenty years had been to him as but a single night. How everyone stared when they heard it! After many talk-filled hours, the gathering broke up. Rip's daughter took him home to live with her.

During the twenty years which Rip had slept away on the mountainside, great changes had taken place. The little village in which he had been born was no longer a colony of the British king. It was now part of the United States. While Rip had been sleeping peacefully, a fierce war had been fought. Now he was no longer an Englishman but an American.

Old Rip Van Winkle spent the rest of his days quite happily. He would sit on the bench in front of the village inn, where for hours he enjoyed the company not only of some of his old friends who still lived, but of the many children who clustered about him, eager to hear stories of the long ago. And the story they loved best was the wonderful tale of the strange little men on the mountain whose ninepins made the sound of thunder, and whose flagons of ale had put Rip Van Winkle to sleep for twenty long years.

John Alden

"WHAT can I do but obey!" said the young man to himself. "Captain Standish is my best friend, my second father. But how can I bring myself to give up the dearest thing in the world for his sake? Was ever a man more miserable than I?"

So spoke John Alden to himself, as he stumbled along through the woods. And indeed, the situation was a heartbreaking one.

John Alden had come to America with the Pilgrims. It was Miles Standish's great daring and fearless leadership that had saved the Pilgrims from massacre by the Indians. Everyone owed a debt of gratitude to their brave leader.

But John Alden owed him more than anyone else, for Miles Standish was his closest friend. The brave captain had taken the young man to his heart. He had taken him into his home, had shared his bed and his meager food with him. How proud had John Alden been of their friendship.

The older man and his young friend had shared many confidences, yet there was one secret that John Alden had confided to no one. That was his love for the Puritan maid, Priscilla. He hoped to ask her to be his wife.

But an extraordinary thing had happened. That very afternoon, Captain Standish had said, "John, I would speak to you of something that has been on my heart for a long time. I love the maiden Priscilla. But although I am bold enough on the field of battle, when it comes to telling a young girl of my love, I am overcome with shyness. I ask you, as my friend and comrade, will you go to Priscilla and tell her of my love? Tell her that I would be the happiest man in the world if she would become my wife."

John Alden was aghast. For a moment he sat as if turned to stone. Then he said, "My friend, it would be much better if you told her yourself."

"Oh, no," answered Miles Standish. "You are young and handsome. You have the gift of talking skillfully and gracefully. Old soldier that I am, I can only speak bluntly, as one talks to soldiers. That is not the way to talk to a gentle lady. In the name of friendship, will you not do this for me?"

In the name of friendship! Those words seemed to ring in John Alden's ears. He could not say "No". And so, smothering every other impulse, he set forth on the errand.

Slowly he made his way through the woods, to Priscilla's modest dwelling. As he drew near, he heard her sweet voice, singing as she sat at her spinning wheel. Oh, how could he bear to give her up!

He stepped quickly into the room. With a glad smile Priscilla rose to greet him and offer him a chair. Her heart beat fast at the sight of the youth, for unbeknownst to him, she had loved him for a long time. When she asked him the reason for his visit, her voice trembled with hope that he would say the words she longed to hear. But John Alden, faithful to his trust, spoke only of his friend's love.

For a moment the maiden sat, amazed and distracted. Then she looked long and searchingly into his eyes, and said in a low, sweet voice, "Why don't you speak for yourself, John?"

John Alden's heart leaped with joy. He took a step forward, as if to clasp her in his arms. But then he remembered. He stopped short, and turning around, ran from the cottage.

He did not know what to do. For many hours he sat alone in the woods. The thought of bringing back Priscilla's answer to Captain Standish filled him with anguish. Slowly he made his way home, and in halting, embarrassed tones, told his friend what Priscilla had said.

In a towering rage Standish rose to his feet. "Faithless friend!" he shouted. "How could you be such a black-hearted villain! To go behind my back and seek to steal the love of the woman I hold dearest in the world! Our friendship has meant nothing to you. Traitor!"

So great was the captain's anger that John Alden truly thought Standish would lay hands on him.

"Why don't you speak for yourself, John?"

Suddenly a man burst into the room. "Captain Standish!" he cried. "The Indians are attacking! Come quickly!"

Without a moment's hesitation, Captain Standish reached for his gun and strode from the room. John Alden followed as they ran toward the meetinghouse. Quickly Captain Standish rounded up a group of men and ordered them to different positions to defend the settlement.

In the heat of the battle, John Alden saw little of Miles Standish. When the beleaguered colonists finally fought off the Indians, John heard that Standish, with a small group of men, had set forth in pursuit of the fleeing Indians.

Days went by with no word from Captain Standish or his men. And then one day, the men came back without their leader. They had a sad story to tell. Their brave captain had been captured by the Indians and had undoubtedly been killed.

Everyone in the little colony felt sick at heart at this terrible news, and John Alden felt worse than anyone else, for he could not forget that his friend had left him in bitter anger. But now that Miles Standish was dead, there was no reason why he should not marry Priscilla, and they set the wedding for a day in Spring.

Their wedding day dawned. It was a beautiful day, and everyone in the settlement had gathered in the crude little church. The young bride stood with glowing eyes as she held her beloved's hand. The wedding ceremony was about to begin. All eyes were fixed on the young couple. Suddenly a voice was heard from behind the crowd.

"John Alden!" said the voice. John Alden stood transfixed. There before his very eyes, stood the sturdy figure of Miles Standish. The captain's clothes were in rags. For one long moment he stood there, while the people gazed in astonishment. Then he strode forward and grasped John Alden's hand.

"Forgive me!" he said. "I have been wrong. I was angry and hurt and I was unfair to you, my friend. In the long nights when I lay in the woods, hiding from the Indians, I had plenty of time to think and to search my heart. How could I ever have doubted that you were my friend? Forgive my hot temper and my harsh words, and let us be friends again!"

Then John Alden embraced his friend and said, "Let all be forgotten, except that we were and will be friends for the rest of our lives."

Johnny Appleseed

THE WANDERING PLANTER

"DADDY, I want something to eat! Daddy, I'm thirsty!" little Billy and Mary Stover cried, as they sat huddled in the back of the bouncing wagon. The wagon was loaded high with the pots and pans and blankets and clothes that the Stover family had taken with them when they started out into the unsettled territory of the Middle West, where they were going to build their new home.

"There'll be something to eat and drink in a little while, children," Mr. Stover answered, with a cheerfulness he did not feel. For where, where, in this wild land could they expect to find any food? In his heart he was praying for a miracle to help them.

Then, suddenly, little Billy cried out, "Look, daddy, look! Apple trees! Over there on the left!" And, sure enough, there was a whole orchard of young trees, heavy with fruit, appearing like the miracle Mr. Stover had prayed for.

"This must be the work of Johnny Appleseed," Mr. Stover cried thankfully. "May the Lord bless him to the end of his days."

Wherever he found a spot . . . he planted seeds . . .

This was *indeed* the gift of Johnny Appleseed — the same kind of gift he had made to hundreds of other pioneer families like the Stovers. For Johnny Appleseed, whose real name was Jonathan Chapman, had set out as a young man, all alone, into the unexplored wilderness, with a bag of apple seeds over his shoulder. Wherever he found a spot that looked right to him, he planted his seeds and continued on.

For forty-six years he had planted this unexpected treasure for other settlers to find, over an area of 100,000 square miles. And in all the forty-six years that Johnny Appleseed spent making his way alone in the wilds and forest lands, among bears, wolves, wild hogs, poisonous snakes, and savage Indian tribes, he never carried a gun. He believed that it was a sin to kill any living thing, even a mosquito. And in all that time, no harm ever came to him! The Indians became his friends, and perhaps even the animals could tell that he meant them no injury.

No one knows where Johnny Appleseed finally was laid to rest, but in the spring, when the apple orchards of Pennsylvania, Ohio, and Indiana are in bloom, the deeds of this brave and loving-hearted man are brought to mind by the sweet perfume of the apple blossoms.